Visionshi

SAFE S

John Hayes is an NHS registered hypnotherapist specialising in the treatment of anxiety and panic.

SAFE SPACE

A self-help manual & practitioner's guide for treating anxiety and panic

---

John Hayes

VISIONSHIP BOOKS

First edition
Published in Great Britain in 2008 by Visionship Books

A Visionship Books paperback

Printed and bound in Great Britain by
Sarsen Press Ltd, Winchester

Visionship Books

St. Thomas House,
7 St Thomas Street,
Winchester SO23 9GN,
England

Registered office

www.visionship.co.uk

For Sami

Preface

By David Slater

There are very few weeks when I fail to come across some new self-help book or fail to be sent one in the mail to review. There are very few these days that actually impress me. Many just seem to trade on their name. Some regurgitate what has been produced many times before by other authors, often producing mediocre material hardly worth a second glance. These are the authors and books that, in all honesty, have very little to offer and perhaps have the merit only to prop the leg of that wobbling coffee table that has been annoying you for so long.

John Hayes is far from being such an author and his new book, SAFE SPACE, is far from being such a book. John, a well qualified and experienced Hypnotherapist, delivers a fresh and original message to his readership in a book which is both well written and very readable.

He is a skilled and thought-provoking practitioner and this comes out clearly in SAFE SPACE. It is a book written about a subject to which most of us can only too readily relate, Panic and Anxiety.

When I was first approached by John to read the first draft of his book in March 2006 I have to admit initially my heart sank and my mind echoed the thought " Oh dear, not another". There are books written on this subject which would fill many shelves of a therapist's bookcase – and more than likely stay there unread. It was John's infectious enthusiasm and commitment that led me to agree to the reading and I will always look back on that day as a day of celebration. It was one of the best decisions that I have made since becoming a reviewer, some 15 years ago, for the Hypnotherapy Association.

This book stands in a class of its own. Indeed, in my opinion, it stands head and shoulders above the vast majority dedicated to Anxiety and Panic. It is not only John's erudition that leads me to say this although that is important. Here is a man who is putting his professional head upon the block and is doing something that far too few professionals do. He is acknowledging that anxiety and panic can be approached and dealt with from a variety of different angles. Yes, he is an experience Hypnotherapist but he does not simply promote this as the all powerful therapy to be used to the exclusion of others. He brings in major elements of Neuro Linguistic programming, Hypnotherapy, Psychotherapy and also, I am delighted to see as a professional counsellor myself, Counselling. Each therapy has something unique to offer and the patient who will benefit the most is the one who is able to receive the "combined approach" as it were.

There has long been an antipathy between counselling organizations and the hypnotherapy bodies – the former having very little positive to say about the latter. John has taken an original and brave stance here which I feel will do much in breaking down the barriers so that therapies and therapists will be seen as elements of a whole rather than an entire and isolated answer in themselves. There may be some professionals who reject this but to me it is an honest approach and I feel can do nothing but good to our caring professions and the patient's understanding of them.

The book is written with deep understanding of the subject and of the needs of people – professional and lay. It is as a result of this that I can see this book being of use not only to the practitioner/therapist but also to the self-helper/client. It is a book which can be read at different levels, the different types of reader taking from it just what they need or desire.

Largely it is clear of jargon. When there is any, John always endeavours to explain it so that the layperson can understand what is being discussed. Personally, I see it as a useful tool which could be used between patient and practitioner. There is a wealth of information here which could be excellent material for therapeutic discussion and planning. I feel, also, it would have an excellent place in any organization which was planning training for those working in the field of helping people with anxiety and panic disorders.

This is a well thought- out book. The use of case studies is excellent and the section named "Tools for Change" is second to none, along with the following section on Procedure. The book is well worth investing in just for these alone.

As a Clinical Hypnotherapist and reviewer of related books for over 15 years now I have no hesitation in recommending this book to you, be you a professional or a person seeking answers and help. You will leave the book feeling well informed, well guided and truly motivated to put John's ideas into practice for yourself. I am also convinced that you will leave the book having undergone a profound and positive change in your approach and thinking in relation to anxiety and panic and its treatment.

I recommend you invest in this book as it will change your life for the better. Of this I have no doubt whatsoever!

David C Slater, BA, DHyp, MASC, MHA(RegHyp), DSC, Dip Counselling Clinical Hypnotherapist and Counsellor.

Contents

Acknowledgements

It is my opinion that any book written about a subject such as anxiety and panic, including this one, can only provide a glimpse of a piece of life's multilayered, multifaceted and constantly evolving jigsaw. As such, it is inevitably limited to my own particular viewpoint which may well have shifted since I wrote the book, and which will no doubt one day be proved antiquated and even wrong.

Nevertheless, regardless of the merits of my position, I would like to acknowledge and thank all my family and friends who have nudged me along the path to where I am now.

I would also like to thank Rebecca Hiscock for instilling into me the confidence and belief necessary to begin the book. To Sam, for inspiring me to write the book largely jargon free and for providing me with the eloquent and candid diary I have used to illustrate it. To David Slater, Melanie White and Anthony Lane, I would like to thank for their wisdom, expertise, gentle criticism and invaluable time. To those people who were either indifferent to or sceptical about whether or not the book would meet the expectations set out in the original proposal, I would like to thank for fuelling my desire to do my best to meet them.

Lastly, I would like to thank my wife, Denize, whose love and support, I know, would not have altered one jot had this book never been written.

Disclaimer

The concepts and techniques provided in this book are not original in that they already exist as components of other models and procedures. I have merely pieced them together in order to form a model and procedure that is specific to the treatment of anxiety and panic. To facilitate the formation of such a stand alone model and procedure I have renamed and adapted some concepts and techniques and have used a different language to describe them.

All the terms relating to aspects of the internal world and highlighted in italics have been chosen and defined specifically to aid in the comprehension of the Safe Space model and procedure. These definitions do not aspire to improve upon, substitute or negate other definitions used in other models.

If some fragments of the scripts for hypnosis bear resemblance to other scripts devised by other practitioners, the similarities are either not intentional or have been included in the belief that they are standard hypnotic language strategies and expressions.

The story of Sam and all other case histories included in this book are only true in that they could have occurred. For those stories based on true stories, to whom they originally occurred is only known to myself and to the protagonists themselves. Even they may be bemused by the changes and alterations I have made, grafting one story to another, deliberately mixing and altering events, modifying experiences, changing names, ages and family backgrounds. Suffice it to say that the secondary characters involved in each story have their own version of events, their own histories and their own reasons for acting in the manner they did, which neither the protagonists nor I will ever know.

Limitations

The Safe Space procedure is specific to anxiety and panic that originates from an event or set of circumstances rooted in the near or distant past.

The Safe Space procedure does not purport to significantly aid in the treatment of long term cases of anxiety and panic associated with depression, addictions, amnesia or psychiatric states of dissociated personality disorders such as schizophrenia.

The procedure is not effective when the perceptions and feelings of the person using the procedure are altered by alcohol or recreational drugs.

The theory and techniques offered in this book have been included to provide the tools to carry out the tasks outlined in the Safe Space procedure. They have not been designed as a "crash course" in hypnotherapy or psychotherapy and should not be viewed or used as such.

SAFE SPACE

Prologue

Who this book is for - The role of trance - Duration of procedure - The case history example
My own personal bias - Notes for practitioners

This book is about that uncomfortable, sometimes overwhelming and often self-defeating experience of existence that wells up inside us when we feel unsafe. More specifically, it is about anxiety and panic that are rooted to some personal past experience, rather than being a natural response to any real threat to our safety.

As human beings we all experience anxiety that is rooted to some drama or other in our lives because none of us can control everything that happens around us, least of all Mother Nature and the intentions of others. Yet as human beings we all strive to grow and evolve, to satisfy our desires and break free from our fears.

Who this book is for

This book is designed as both a *guide* for practitioners working to help clients overcome anxiety or panic, and as a *self-help manual* for those wishing to determine their own healing process. The book draws from both the worlds of hypnotherapy and psychotherapy. On the assumption that practitioners tend to know more about one than the other, and that the average lay reader may know little about either, I have endeavoured to provide in the first three chapters all the theory and techniques necessary to carry out the tasks outlined in the procedure, chapter four. No knowledge of hypnotherapy or psychotherapy is necessary to benefit from this book.

For those using the book as a ***self-help manual*** I have written the procedure using the vernacular *you* form, as if addressing *you* the *self-helper*. Engaging in self-help does not mean that you have to work alone. There is no reason why you cannot co-work with someone wishing to achieve a similar goal. Indeed, such a partnership can often make for a more stimulating and fulfilling experience.

For ***practitioners***, which I include hypnotherapists, psychotherapists, counsellors and GPs, *Safe Space* offers a stand alone model that draws on the psychotherapeutic concept of sub-personalities and combines it with the accelerating techniques of hypnotherapy. In addition, a cognitive process prompts the client to understand, explore and direct their own healing process. The model and procedure attempt to highlight the areas in which hypnotherapy and psychotherapy overlap, and I have endeavoured to use a common language that can be understood by both from within their own frames of reference. I hope that this book will go some small way to helping strengthen the bridge that unites these two disciplines. *Safe Space* is particularly relevant to Ericksonian hypnotherapists and psychotherapists with training in Gestalt, Jungian, voice dialogue, psychodrama, psycho synthesis, transactional analysis and ego-state therapy.

The role of trance

Some of the tasks outlined in the procedure use visualizations. These are most effective when carried out in a light to medium state trance using hypnosis or self-hypnosis. For those unfamiliar with hypnotic trance, this book includes techniques for inducing trance and a step by step procedure for both hypnosis and self-hypnosis. The procedure for self-hypnosis is specifically designed for those using the book as a self-help manual and requires no previous experience or knowledge of trance.

Duration of procedure

For those using the book as a self-help manual, the procedure can be carried out over a period of between four and eight weeks. Choosing the shorter four week period requires investing around three hours a week of your time. Choosing the longer eight week period requires around two hours a week. Although the procedure can be carried out in much less time, some parts of the procedure may require a period of digestion. Advice on where and when to carry out the procedure can be found at the beginning of chapter four, *The Procedure*.

For practitioners, a seven week period is advised, with one session per week. Details of procedure duration, session frequency and time boundaries can be found at the beginning of chapter four, *The Procedure*.

The case history example

I am indebted to many professionals who have either instilled into me or coaxed out of me the conviction necessary to write this book. The inspiration for it, however, came from a client called Sam, a once long term sufferer of anxiety and panic with whom I had the pleasure to work with. During our sessions together, Sam kept a journal of his thoughts and feelings. It is, in my opinion, an extremely candid, insightful and eloquently written account of how anxiety, our pasts and our personalities are all inextricably linked. Sam kindly gave me permission to use the journal in order to illustrate some of the concepts and procedures outlined in this book.

My first impression of Sam when he presented himself to me was that of a man who seemed pretty sure of himself. Not only did he come across as charming, articulate and insightful, he was also an extremely adept and eloquent story teller capable of lulling his listener, myself, away from his anxious and panicky feelings and into stories *about* his anxious and panicky feelings. It took a deliberate effort on my part to extricate myself from his elegant narratives and notice that seeping out of him was a fear and sadness that seemed to well up from deep within and which, on occasion, threatened to overflow.

Like many of my clients, Sam came to me because his anxiety and panic were both hindering his career and complicating his personal life. When I met Sam, he had already attributed the initial cause of his anxiety and panic to two experiences that occurred in close succession to one another when he was seven years old.

The first of these events was the manner in which Sam experienced his parent's separation and the world view Sam subsequently formed. The second experience Sam believed lay at the root of his anxiety and panic was an acute humiliation he suffered at school when, unable to recite the seven times table in front of his class, he wet himself. To compound Sam's sense of shame and unworthiness, his teacher deemed it appropriate that Sam wore a badge with the number seven on it until Sam was capable of reciting the times table correctly.

During our sessions together, Sam identified other experiences which he felt attributed to his anxiety and panic and which influenced his ability to deal with them. However, the change in his relationship to the way he viewed and experienced the above events were key to him overcoming his anxiety and panic.

The following extract from Sam's journal shows how Sam came to view himself in relation to his anxiety and panic. Sam came to understand himself in this way after much contemplation, discussion and self assessment. His journal was not a required part of the procedure, but was born out of his own desire to record his thoughts and feelings.

Sam's journal: The root of my anxiety

"..hidden behind all my responses crouched something dark, obscure and amorphous that I feared would, at any moment, leap out and ambush me. I would never have admitted to its existence, perhaps because it was so well camouflaged I could pretend to myself that it was not there, but sometimes it glinted at my denial, like a shard of light reflecting off a broken mirror, and I realized that whatever lurked inside would not let me forget how one of my parents had let the other take me away. Was I not valuable or important enough to fight for? My subsequent need to feel worthy in the eyes of others was my prime motivator for success, the reason I feared failure and the energy behind my competitive nature. I needed to be a winner to be valued. So great was my fear of defeat that I would avoid at all costs situations in which I might lose. The incident with the maths teacher in which I experienced acute public shame was a second, simultaneous blow to my self-esteem. From the moment these two events impacted on me, I constructed a personality upon which such a loss made no obvious mark, but this did not mean that I had not felt the pain of the blows. As a child the knock was masked by an imaginary fantasy world in which I was destined for magical things. In time this fantastical self solidified into a an intense but disarmingly child-like quality which, with training, I used as a ploy to divert intimacy, just like a magician diverts attention away from his slight of hand; but my most skilful trick was not to hide the fact that I was frightened of people but to hide this knowledge from myself.

It takes a wise man to know why he is afraid, and a brave one to admit to it. I was neither. Certainly I was not ready to consider that my tendency to distance myself from the lives of others was no more than a ploy to avoid other people removing themselves from mine. I was merely getting my disappointment in first. Nor was I aware that my underachievement at work was because my fear of

> defeat was so much greater than my desire for success. But the belief that I was unable to risk being harmed through the loss of another's love and through not being valued was a secret even from myself. It tiptoed silently behind me, growing longer and stronger the closer I got to someone, and because of it, almost no-one got near me. Or rather, I did not let them. And when someone did threaten to reveal my vulnerable core, I panicked and I ran away, or I attacked and they ran away from me."

Sam felt anxious and panicky about circumstances which to others may seem unthreatening, despite Sam having at his disposal a substantial array of defensive strategies and personas to deal with such uncomfortable feelings and to rationalize his self-sabotaging behaviour. This notion of having a protective persona that masks our underlying anxiety lies at the heart of the *Safe Space* model.

My own personal bias

To appreciate the aims of this book it is perhaps necessary to take into consideration my own personal bias. Naturally, the passage of time continually nudges us all from one point of view to another in accordance with our particular needs at the time. However, there is one perspective on anxiety and panic that I always keep in mind regardless of where I am standing. It is the view that anxiety and panic form part of a bundle of emotions and feelings that we all naturally experience because we are alive. Or, more pertinently perhaps, because we are all, at some level, aware of the fragile and finite nature of our existence. Viewed in this way, anxiety and panic are not solely responses to external dramas and circumstances, but are part of the condition of being alive. External events such as physical and emotional abuse, rejection, separation, loss and isolation simply inflame the embers of existence, the same embers that fire our passions and which, like certain stars, we only get to glimpse by diverting our gaze onto the thing that triggers the emotions. What makes each one of us special and unique are our personal circumstances and the resources we have at our disposal to respond to them.

One of the things that prompts me to take this view is that implicit in it is the notion that, essentially, we are all united by a common anxiety which binds us to one another and enables us to communicate in a compassionate, intimate and meaningful way. After all, we all want to connect and belong, to feel accompanied and safe, to be able to express how we really feel and feel reasonable sure that we are safe to do so. In other words, we all want a place where we can be ourselves, warts and all. A home.

In practice, of course, home to many is neither harmonious nor safe, but for most people the idea of what a home should be involves a place where family members or friends can grow, evolve and have fun together in relative harmony and safety.

One of the main tasks of this book is to create a unique individual internal *home* that provides the boundaries and resources necessary in order to feel safe and secure on the inside while roaming around the big wide world outside.

A second main task in this book is to readdress those personal dramas that lie at the root of our anxiety and panic and that prompt us to feel more anxious than is really necessary in order to survive. This process does not entail the re-living of painful past experiences, but rather introduces into them aspects of ourselves that have the resources to either change the outcome of the original story or to provide a new perspective on it, thus shifting our relationship to external events and people that previously triggered the memories.

The third main task is to identify the defensive mechanisms we previously engaged to protect ourselves from feeling anxious and panicky and to re-deploy them in more creative and positive tasks.

The end result is, I hope, a more rewarding, intimate and fulfilling relationship with ourselves, our pasts, other people and the world.

Notes for practitioners

Prevailing trends

Whatever the cause of anxiety and panic, western culture seems to have resigned itself to a way of being where personal anxiety, like stress, is accepted as part of the fabric of everyday life.

I don't know that society has become more stressed and life more urgent, whether we have simply become less tolerant of abuse and trauma, or that we simply have more time to deal with them. What I do know is that therapists and GP's are finding their waiting rooms full of people wanting short term solutions to what is often a long term condition. Current medication available has varying degrees of effectiveness, and not everyone wants to take pills to ease their minds.

This shift towards the desire for more short term solutions in the last decade has been reflected in the emergence of companies who offer large organization and institutions short term support, referred to as Employee Assistance Programmes (EAPs), for their employees. By short term, I mean procedures that have a fixed duration, a fixed cost and a means to measure success. In the corporate world of outcomes, products, targets and mission statements, it is not inconceivable that this penchant for offering short term solutions has largely been determined by their cost-effectiveness and manageability. The more cynical minded of us may believe that the primary motive is to reduce the amount of sick leave employees take. The more pragmatic of us may believe that the ability to measure and quantify treatments is that which makes them useful. The popularity of Cognitive Behavioural Therapy (CBT) with large institutions certainly backs up this belief. On an individual level there is also a growing demand for the more solution focused and goal orientated short term approaches like hypnotherapy, neuro-linguistic programming (NLP) and life coaching.

Whether for companies or individuals, short term solutions are what most people seem to want. But can short term approaches effectively address the underlying causes of anxiety and panic? Even if they usefully manage symptoms, will the symptoms keep coming back? *Safe Space* attempts to find a middle ground by using a coherent therapeutic model specific to anxiety and panic and a short term step by step procedure that changes our relationship with the root of anxiety and panic.

The role of practitioner

At the risk of oversimplifying, it could be said that *talking therapies*, of which I include counselling and psychotherapy, tend towards the notion that a practitioner should not lead or influence the client, that interference should be kept to a minimum and, were it possible, to be non-existent. Goal orientated therapies such as hypnotherapy, neuro-linguistic programming and Cognitive Behavioural Therapy lean more towards the idea that the practitioner has a determining role to play in the process of change.

Safe Space attempts to combine and balance the more client-centred, circumspective and exploratory nature of longer term psychotherapy with the more structured directive nature of short term, goal orientated disciplines. It endeavours to be as client centred as possible within the bounds of a short term model. This is exemplified in the first step of the procedure in which the theory and procedure are shared with the client.

This brings to the fore the idea of the practitioner as being *directive* or *leading*. These notions have often been maligned in the world of talking therapies. However, while there may be different levels of transparency within different approaches, it is inevitable that the practitioner will at some level influence the therapeutic process.

Hypnotherapy has never tried to hide the fact that the practitioner can be directive and has sometimes been treated with suspicion because of it. However, just as there are different interventions a hypnotherapist can use, there are crucial differences in the degree of directiveness, ranging from direct suggestion and guided interventions to indirect suggestion, metaphor and analogy. As long as the needs of the client remain paramount, all can be used effectively.

The procedure set out in *Safe Space* focuses on the client constructing and directing their own healing. The practitioner acts as a *responsive guide* who accompanies the client along their journey and supports them when overcoming any obstacles they may encounter. For example, if the client imagines the obstacle to be a "boulder", the *responsive guide* can discuss the composition of the "boulder" and how it got there, elicit and explore ways of getting around it or moving it, and support the client as they attempt to do so. *Responsive guiding* not only helps the client to look at scenarios in alternative ways, but also involves eliciting the tools the client will use to confront, pass, move, eliminate or change their relationship to the "boulder". *Responsive guiding* deals very much with what emerges. The use of hypnosis or self-hypnosis simply helps the client engage with the process of visualizing scenarios on a semi-conscious level that allows them to engage emotionally, while at the same consciously controlling their actions – rather like directing a dream. It is crucial that the practitioner understands and is aware of how their own process affects the client and the therapeutic process.

For those using *Safe Space* as a self-help manual, the role of practitioner is taken by this book.

Concepts that Safe Space draws on

One of the principle concepts *Safe Space* draws from is the idea that the personality can be seen as a collection of sub *personalities* or selves, each with different roles, fears and desires. The first significant systemic book to identify and synthesise the concept of sub personalities was John Rowan's book entitled *Sub personalities – The People Inside Us.* It shows how conceptual systems drawing upon the idea of sub personalities are used by virtually all talking therapies and any adequate personality theory in one form or another, even though they are working independently and may use different terminology. The approaches Rowen connects on this basis include psychoanalysis, Jungian, psycho synthesis, psychodrama, gestalt therapy, voice dialogue, Cognitive Behavioural Therapy, neuro-linguistic programming, transactional analysis and ego state therapy. Rowan, in his book, was dismissive of hypnotherapy. However, in a later book, *Discover Your Sub personalities*, he dedicated a whole chapter to it.

Hypnotherapy has its own procedures based on sub personalities. Roy Hunter's book *Hypnosis for Inner Conflict Resolution* introduces *Parts Therapy*, a procedure in which the hypnotherapist acts as mediator between different and often conflicting *parts* of the client. The *mediator* sets up a dialogue between the *parts* so that negotiation can take place. The aim of negotiation is to reach a compromise or agreement that enables all parts to get their respective needs met while at the same time taking into account the individual as a whole. Hunter draws on the ideas of other hypnotherapists including Charles Tebbit and John Bradshaw.

Practitioners of other approaches are also incorporating into their models the idea of *parts*. Nancy Napier, a marriage and family therapist works with a variation of Parts therapy. In her book *Recreating your SELF: Help for Adult Children of Dysfunctional Families*, Napier provides some self-hypnosis scripts for identifying and healing various *parts*. The clinical psychologists, Hal Stone and Sidra Winkleman refined and developed Voice dialogue, based on the same concept as Parts therapy except that only a light state of trance is used. The clinical psychologists John and Helen Watkins work with ego states, a psychodynamic approach in which techniques of group and family therapy are employed to resolve conflicts between various *ego states* that constitute a *family of self*. Hypnosis is one of the primary tools they use to connect with the different ego states.

Safe Space draws further on the conceptual system of sub personalities by defining a model that is specific to panic and anxiety. It is a stand alone model which provides a bridge between the hypnotherapeutic and psychotherapeutic camps.

Recent shifts in relationship between hypnotherapy and psychotherapy

Throughout their relatively short history, hypnotherapy and psychotherapy have always been irrevocably linked. Freud used hypnosis and was, in some people's eyes, the father of psychoanalysis. In recent years, however, moves by the government to increase regulation have prompted the British Association of Counselling and Psychotherapy (BACP) to actively distance themselves from hypnotherapy.

Subsequent changes in the legislation of the governing bodies meant that hypnotherapy was no longer accepted as a component of counselling/psychotherapy training or practice for the purpose of accreditation. This was seen by various sections of the profession to be effectively de-classifying hypnotherapy as a legitimate psychotherapeutic technique.

The position of the BACP may be in part due to a lack of understanding between the two traditions, no matter how common a root they share. Their stance could be influenced by the different levels of regulation required by the established representatives of Hypnotherapy for their members. For example, not all require their members to receive supervision or to partake in any ongoing Professional Development. Nor is there a requirement on the part of hypnotherapists to partake in a process of self-development or to reflect on their own psychological and emotional history. More pertinently perhaps, hypnotherapy ascribes to no clear model.

If hypnotherapy remains in its current position in relation to psychotherapy there is a danger of it becoming marginalised and the potential gains that psychotherapy and hypnotherapy can offer one another will be lost. This book hopes to go some small way to reaffirm the status of hypnotherapy as an important tool in the process of healing, and to utilise a language that can be understood by both approaches in order that each tradition be mutually enriched by the skills and resources of the other.

The techniques currently used by hypnotherapists to overcome panic and anxiety are extremely successful. The framework outlined in *Safe Space* draws on these techniques and fixes them within the framework of a coherent model. In addition, this model significantly deepens the current procedure by incorporating a client centred cognitive process in which the client can understand, explore and develop their own healing. *Safe Space* also provides analogies to aid this process of comprehension and intervention.

1
Introduction

Anxiety & Panic - Hypnotherapy & Psychotherapy - The Safe Space Model - The Safe Space Procedure

Anxiety and Panic

The symptoms

How many of us have experienced mild anxiety in some form or another, at some time in our lives? All of us, because we are human. Yet the language we use to define our experience of anxiety is often limited to phrases such as *I'm a bit on edge, having a wobble, worried, tense, wound up.*

Anxiety does, however, have specific recognizable symptoms, even if we do not always associate them with anxiety. Often we are not even aware of them, such as grinding our teeth, twitching, rocking, picking at food when we are not hungry, tidying up when everything is tidy, speaking too much or not speaking much at all. Other symptoms associated with more acute states of anxiety are more apparent, such as sweaty palms, rapid shallow breathing, a pounding heart, trembling, shaking, memory loss and vomiting, all accompanied by varying degrees of discomfort, fear or dread.

If you have experienced any of these symptoms, some of you may associate them with anxiety, others with panic. What separates these two, however, is often merely the duration and intensity of the symptoms. One way of describing anxiety is, then, as mild ongoing panic.

The triggers

Whatever the relationship between anxiety and panic, the circumstances and stimuli that *trigger* them vary from person to person. Some are more common than others, for example, driving along motorways, overtaking, crossing bridges, going through tunnels, meeting new people, large groups, Christmas day, confined places, crowded places, high places, foreign places, speaking in public, being interviewed, being shouted at, being laughed at, being abandoned, loss, separation and enforced change.

Other triggers are more specific and individual. I have had clients, for example, whose triggers have included, the sound of water running, the near proximity of stagnant ponds, people with beards, the texture of velvet, the colour purple, the smell of whisky and the word *apricot.*

The cause

It can often feel as if these triggers are what cause our anxiety or panic, when they may simply connect the individual to a previous traumatic experience, sometimes referred to as an *originating event* or *COAX*[1]. The memories belonging to the *originating event* or particular COAX system have a basic theme and contain similar elements to the presenting circumstances, the *triggers*, which connect the person to the feeling experienced in the initial trauma. For example, if the anxiety or panic were triggered while driving along a particular stretch of road, the *originating event* may have been an accident on the same or a similar stretch of road. In these instances, the unconscious mind connects the present situation (the particular stretch of road) to the *originating event* (the accident) and responds to it in a way that the conscious mind often experiences as irrational. i.e. Why should one stretch of road be more dangerous than another almost identical one?

This apparent conflict between the conscious and the unconscious mind can be even more perplexing for sufferers who have no recollection of an *originating event.* For example, an adult who was abandoned as a small child, or who as a baby was subject to highly irregular feeding times. Or simply someone who does not know what the *originating event* is.

For some people there may not have been a single, identifiable *originating event.* Their anxiety may be due to an accumulation of the stresses and strains of everyday life. Or it could be that the event may yet to occur, such as a potential or impending loss, divorce, redundancy, discovery or change.

Others often experience acute anxiety or panic for the first time as a consequence of a relatively insignificant event which does not appear to warrant feelings of unease or distress. On occasion, this is because the feelings associated with a previous *originating event* have lain dormant and have been triggered by a similar albeit less traumatic event or set of

---

[1] *System of condensed experience defined as a specific constellation of memories consisting of condensed experiences (and related feelings and fantasies) from different life periods of the individual* - Rowan *1993*

circumstances. This *trigger* event is often referred to as an *initiating event,* and here is referred to as the *trigger event.*

Sometimes, neither the *originating event* nor the *trigger event* are obviously related to the circumstance which seem to trigger our anxiety. For example, much driving related anxiety is experienced by excellent drivers with no prior driving related trauma. The act of driving may simply be a conduit for issues around control. For example, a person who feels they are no longer in control of the direction their life is taking may feel particularly insecure "behind the wheel", especially when the road appears to force the driver into going in one direction or another, like dual carriageways and tunnels.

One client of mine called Marta, for example, began to panic whenever she had to drive through a one-way system. Marta was a forty-year old divorcee and her fear, it transpired, was not connected to any previous experience in a one-way system, but to her relationship with her ex-husband and children. Once Marta told the following story, the connection between these became apparent: Several years earlier, she had taken up the offer of a short term contract in Canada, even though her husband and children could not join her. Everyday on her way to her new job she was forced to drive through a one-way system. One day she returned home to the news that her husband wanted a divorce. Marta was distraught and not only was she unable to persuade him to change his mind but she also lost the battle for custody of the children. When Marta finally returned to England, she met another man with whom she wished to start a new life. However, her children were still extremely important to her and she feared that, were she to commit to a new relationship, she would distance herself from her children even further. Although Marta may not have been aware of this fear, the first time she experienced panic was while driving through a one-way system to meet her new partner for the first time. Given Marta's recent history, it is plausible that a part of her connected one-way systems with her "single-minded" decision to temporarily leave her family in order to pursue her career, and the subsequent painful consequences of this decision. Naturally, the story had many other components to it, but it illustrates how things in the external world, like one-way systems, can symbolize internal ones.

Another example of a *trigger* not directly related to the *cause* is that of a gentleman called Tom who came to see me because he found himself uncontrollably angry and panicky every time someone parked their car in his private parking space. This space was one of several at the back of the block of flats where he lived. Given that all were identical and it therefore made little difference who parked where, it was not unusual for another resident, or indeed a non-resident to park in the space allocated to Tom. So strong were Tom's feelings about someone "stealing" his space that he would often stay awake at night to guard it. His panic and anger, it transpired, had nothing to do with his car parking rights being infringed upon. Rather, people that "trespassed" on his space symbolized an abuse he had suffered as a child in someone else's car. Tom felt both deeply ashamed and angry about this event and until our sessions together he had never once in his life talked about the abuse. When Tom did finally divulge it, his fear of people "stealing" his space notably subsided.

Another example of an external trigger that mirrors an internal belief is that of a young lady called Aisha who initially came to me because she was afraid of snakes, which in my opinion is a healthy fear. When it became apparent that Aisha rarely came into contact with snakes I suggested, wrongly in hindsight, that she reassess her need for therapy to overcome the problem. However, she insisted on continuing with the sessions and, perhaps to justify her decision, she reeled off a list of other things she feared and felt anxious about. These included being attacked by a one-eyed monster and being responsible for the life of her partner whom she believed would be fated to die horribly if she were to have sexual intercourse with him before they were married. Given that the young lady had never met a one-eyed monster, had never had a particularly traumatic experience with a snake or had ever had sexual intercourse with anyone, I was intrigued to discover the cause of her anxiety. That is, until she told me about her Islamic education, which included the belief that sex before marriage was a sin punished by hellfire. I immediately identified this world view as the cause of her irrational fears. However, as we worked to dissolve this connection, her anxiety about snakes, one-eyed monsters and pre-marital sex did not subside. It was only after exploring how Aisha benefited from holding onto her fears that she discovered how her fears gave her a reason, and permission, to avoid the transition from child to adult. Or rather, how she could maintain being looked after and protected by her parents and avoid taking responsibility for her own actions and accepting the risks involved.

In a nutshell, Aisha just didn't want to "grow up". Naturally there were other reasons, and very good ones too, for Aisha's reluctance to leave her family nest, but her particular religious beliefs had served, to some degree, as an excuse not to step out into the big wide world. A world in which the snake represented her inherent sexuality and in which the one-eyed monster represented the potential dangers that lurk behind ever corner. Subsequent to the sessions, Aisha's spiritual beliefs not only remained intact, but actually grew stronger.

In both the above stories, those things which triggered anxiety and panic existed in the external world as objects and actions, like driving through one-way systems, someone "stealing" a car parking space, snakes and sexual intercourse. I would never underestimate how real the connection is between anxiety and the external triggers. Nor would I ever claim to know for sure what the "real" cause of anxiety and panic is. Perhaps one can never be sure. What I do know is that, sometimes, what we perceive to be a *trigger* often simply mirrors or symbolizes something else.

The reaction

Whatever the *cause* or *trigger* of anxiety and panic, how we respond and react to them tends to include several common coping strategies. If you have not experienced acute anxiety or panic, or your recollection of them is vague, the following extract from *Sam's journal* may jog your memory or help fuel your imagination.

The extract begins as Sam is preparing for a job interview. It is a group interview in which six other competing candidates will be present. The right hand column includes some of the symptoms Sam experiences.

Sam's journal: My experience of anxiety and panic before an interview

I am in my bedroom deciding what to wear. I glance up at the clock on the wall. Only fifteen minutes left before I must leave. My partner, Liz, hovers in the background while I rummage in the wardrobe for another shirt.	**- Time anxiety** **- Indecision**

"How about the white shirt with those grey trousers?" suggests Liz.

I put them on.

"Great," says Liz.

"Too flashy!" I reply, taking off the white shirt and putting on a blue one.

"Great," says Liz.

"You said great about the white shirt!" I snap.

- Irritation

Liz holds her hands up in the air.

"I know," I apologise. "Whatever I wear will be fine, right?"

- Rationalisation

Wrong. What you wear is crucial. You'll be in the spot light. All eyes will be on you. Wear the wrong thing and they will expose you.

- Predicting worst case scenario

Of course, nobody speaks these words, because the part of me that communicates the message transmits it in the form of a shadowy, amorphous feeling. My rational mind tries to suppress it.

It's only a job interview, I tell myself, *but then again it makes sense to minimalize the risk, right? Yes, clothes must be carefully chosen.*

- Collusion with irrational thoughts

I study myself in the mirror.

"My hair!"

It is still wet.

A flicker of panic ignites. I glance at the clock again. Two minutes left.

- Time anxiety

"I knew it. I'm going to be late," I complain accusingly to Liz who, car keys in hand, is waiting patiently by the door.

- Transferring responsibility

Once in the car, I fumble for the keys.

"Where are my keys? They were here in my pocket!"

- Memory loss

Liz holds out the keys and offers to drive.

"No, you drove me to that last horrendous interview," I say, taking the keys and gripping the steering wheel with both hands. As I reach for the gear stick, my sweaty palm leaves a black stain. I crunch into first gear and narrowly miss the car in front.

- Mistrust

- Sweating

- Clumsiness

"Unlucky," jokes Liz, referring to my inability to hit a model of car which we both share a particular dislike. I reply with a glare and a stony silence. I then proceed to spout a catalogue of potential disasters that will conspire to make me late; traffic jams, a flat tyre, a petrol leak, a Martian invasion.

- Loss of humour

- Pessimism & conspiracy theories

I arrive safely and on time.

"Good luck," says Liz, as I try to get out of the car. I sit back down, undo the seat belt and try again.

"Have you got everything?" asks Liz.

I pat my pockets without noticing what is in them. My heart is pounding. "Yes," I say. Liz drives off into the distance, waving and I am left alone in front of a huge building that reminds me of my first school.

- Not listening
- Pounding heart

I am on my own now, I tell myself. *Have I got everything?* This time I really do check. *Interview slip? Check. Mobile phone off?* I push the relevant button, the phone turns off, then mysteriously turns itself on again. My heart pounds faster. I frantically push all the buttons. The phone turns off. The panic subsides.

- Loss of self-control

I take a deep breath.

Everything will be ok, I reassure myself.

To be on the safe side, I go through for the umpteenth time the answer I memorised the previous night.

- Obsessional behaviour

Yes, I am completely committed to...to...I am completely committed to...to what? Committed to what?

- Memory loss

I reach inside my jacket pocket for my notes.

My notes! Where are my notes? I've forgotten my notes! I knew this would happen!

My heart pounds harder. I feel dizzy. I am going to faint. I don't faint.

- Fear of fainting

Run! my instincts tell me. *Run!*

- Avoidance

At this point in Sam's story one of two things could happen. Either Sam does run, thus avoiding the interview, or he decides to go through with it.

If Sam avoids the interview his anxiety and panic will subside. He may even manage to convince himself that he doesn't want the job. If Sam goes ahead with the interview, he may perform brilliantly or he may stammer, freeze or speak gobbledegook.

Coping strategies

Whatever occurs, Sam's experience of anxiety and panic included four common strategies to reduce his uncomfortable feelings: 1.) He tried to rationalize the situation by reminding himself it was only an interview. 2.) He tried to minimize the risk by choosing clothes most appropriate for the occasion. 3.) He prepared himself by memorising a speech. 4.) He attempted to avoid the interview when he no longer felt in control of the situation.

The context of Sam's anxiety would have made little difference to the strategies he employed to reduce it. For example, had his anxiety been triggered by driving on busy roads, he would have reacted in much the same way: He would have rationalized by reminding himself that he was a capable driver. He would have minimalized the risk by slowing down. He would have prepared by planning his route carefully so as to avoid busy roads. He would have stopped the car or taken an alternative route if he felt out of control.

The downward spiral of panic

Although Sam's strategies may reduce his feelings of anxiety and panic in the short term, they may be debilitating in the long term. This is made more likely by the following three factors which can feed off and perpetuate each other, leading to the fear of an attack growing in the mind and thus an increase in the likelihood of one occurring: 1.) Sam becomes over vigilant and sensitized to minor bodily symptoms that he may have previously ignored. 2.) He misinterprets what is happening and begins to believe that the worst possible consequences are the ones most likely to occur. 3.) He starts to avoid certain situations for fear of having a panic attack, progressively losing his ability to cope with them.

The fight or flight response

Those who are aware of having experienced any of the above symptoms often believe that their responses are irrational or unnatural. However, without the physiological mechanisms that prompt anxiety and panic the human race may have long ago become extinct. What we experience as anxiety and panic is a by-product of a natural physiological response to danger - the so-called *fight or flight response.* It can be traced back thousands of years to our ancestors who, when confronted by a physical threat such as a lion, had to fight or run just like other animals. In such situations the sympathetic autonomic nervous system prompts noradrenalin to be released into the body causing the following changes to take place in the metabolism: 1.) The heart pumps faster and arteries dilate to increase the blood supply to the muscles in the limbs. 2.) Blood pressure rises. 3.) Blood vessels supplying the skeletal muscles dilate increasing the nourishing and waste removal processes thus enabling the muscle to work better. 4.) The spleen contracts, increasing the volume of blood circulating. 5.) Breathing speeds up to take in more oxygen. 6.) Sweating cools the body.

This combination of physiological changes ensures that the individual can draw on his or her optimum strength, speed and dexterity. In the distant past, much of our anxiety would have revolved around external threats such as large predators and, therefore, we would have been more concerned about protecting our external boundaries, hence the need for our bodies to be primed to attack and defend. This same reflex action lies at the heart of anxiety and panic. Today, for many of us, these external physical threats to our safety have been minimalized. Yet we seem to have resigned ourselves to a way of being where anxiety, like stress, is accepted as part of the fabric of everyday life. We may not have lions to deal with any more, but we do have other threats, both immediate, potential and perceived. More often than not these threats are social and psychological rather than physical, for example, redundancy, divorce, isolation and abandonment. It is often not the body we need to function at its optimum, but our minds. Our instincts, though, do not necessarily distinguish between types of threat, unless we train them to do so. This often means that our natural fight or flight response can impede us when we need to think calmly and rationally, just at it did with *Sam*.

Definition of anxiety

Anxiety could then be defined as a response to a message from the brain to the body that something is not quite right and that the space we occupy is not safe. This space can be our body, our home, our family, the group or community we belong to, the ideas and beliefs we adhere to, or the memories we hold on to. Some of these spaces are protected by their own natural boundaries like skin and walls. Other boundaries we create ourselves, such as borders, rules and laws.

The external world

Of all the places we inhabit, perhaps the most immediate is our *body*, the boundary of which we protect in order to ward off external physical threats such as predators, illness, disease, cold and heat. How we do this is determined by a number of factors including location, climate, culture, economy and historical context. For example, if you are fair-skinned and it was hot and sunny, you may decide to put on a good deal of sun tan lotion, a hat and a pair of sun glasses. If it then started to turn cold and rainy, you may put up an umbrella or put on a coat.

To further protect our physical *selves,* we have homes with doors, walls and fences we can shut, lock and bolt in order to create a safe space. Our homes are determined by the same factors as our bodies. For example, if we were living in a cold and rainy environment we would ideally have a home designed and built with this in mind. If we lived two hundred years ago on the plains of North America, a tepee that we could move around may be more suitable.

Unlike our bodies, our home can be inhabited by more than one person. This is usually with people or animals of our choice such as family members, pets, close friends, people with similar convictions, needs and beliefs. As with our bodies, if we feel that the boundaries of our homes are likely to be breached without our consent, we may feel anxious, and if we feel powerless to protect them, we may panic.

Fortunately, for most of us, our homes are protected by another larger space such as the community, tribe, country or belief system we belong to or adhere to, each with their own boundaries, borders and laws. We may not have so much control over their boundaries, but decisions regarding their protection are made based on the same climatic, geographic, historical, cultural and economic factors. For example, an ever increasing number of individual countries in the West attempt to increase the safeness of their space by banding together as member states of a unified community called Europe. Meanwhile, in the East, an increasing number of ex-member states of another community, once called the USSR, stride out in search of their own independent safe space. Simultaneously, groups affiliated to different belief systems including Christianity, Judaism, Buddhism and Islam strive to find a way to share their *space* while engaging in an often violent struggle to overcome the historical events that led to their being separated in the first place.

How communities respond to potential threats is less within the sphere of influence of the individual, simply because so many people inhabit them. Each community then has its own succession of politicians, heads of state, leaders and representatives. Just like the body and the home, when the majority of inhabitants of one of these *larger spaces* feel threatened, the act of protecting the space often results in conflict born out of anxiety and, in cases where the group feels it has lost its ability to defend its space, in panic.

The internal world

While all this goes on out there in the external world, each of us, one of billions of individuals, experience pretty much the same within our own unique internal worlds. And just as the external world is influenced by changing physical circumstances, so our internal world is influenced by changing and often conflicting emotional needs and desires.

Unlike the external world, this internal landscape has no obvious navigational references or pre-conceived boundaries like trees, buildings, walls, people, borders or laws. It is not something that we can touch, smell, taste or "see". It is an intangible world composed of enigmatic symbols, complex patterns and invisible pathways. In our dreams we enter this internal world and glimpse how different aspects of ourselves act out their respective desires, fears and needs. However, rarely are we able to consciously influence dreams while they occur, and so diverse are the ways in which the different aspects of ourselves are expressed that it becomes difficult to identify or interpret them.

Fortunately, clues to this internal world also exist in the external world. Here too, the different aspects of ourselves battle to satisfy or avoid often conflicting desires, fears and needs. How many of us, for example, have woken up in the morning and found ourselves embroiled in the following futile battle between a part of us that wants to stay in bed a little longer, and a part that thinks we should get up.

Relax, one part says. *Listen to your body. You need to snuggle under this soft, warm duvet a little bit longer if you are going to work effectively. Just one more minute.*

Yeah, right, replies another part, *and then you'll be late for work, get the sack and have no work at all.*

Both parts have the individual's best interests at heart, but they want completely different things.

Sam experiences the same internal struggle while trying to decide which clothes to wear for the interview. On the one hand, Sam was drawn towards the more muted combinations of greys and browns, the choice perhaps of a shy, withdrawn part of Sam that did not want to draw much attention to itself. On the other hand, Sam wanted to wear a brighter, bolder combination, the choice perhaps of a more confident, outgoing part of Sam.

These two apparently opposing parts no doubt had their own very good reasons and arguments for getting Sam to meet their respective needs. However, the part with the most immediate or critical need in the presenting circumstances often dominates, ignoring the needs of the other part. In the case of Sam, it was the shy and insecure part that dominated because Sam ended up wearing the muted combination.

These parts are often referred to as *sub-personalities*[2], and in the *Safe Space* model as *selves.* They can be extremely powerful, and if their respective needs are not met, they have many, often debilitating, ways of getting themselves heard, such as provoking headaches and bad dreams, twitching and red flushes. Although Sam's little internal squabble about which clothes to wear may not have been life-threatening, when *selves* disagree over important issues to do with personal relationships and professional decisions, they can cause a considerable amount of personal anxiety and distress if one or other is not listened to and their needs not met. Many of us, for example, have to deal with both a *self* that demands independence and freedom within a relationship, and a part that requires the security afforded by a restrictive set of relationship rules.

Whether or not our different emotional needs can be attributed to different semi-autonomous *selves* or *sub-personalities* is not of concern here. The concept of *selves* simply helps us to navigate and manage an otherwise shadowy, amorphous internal landscape.

To aid in this process of navigating this internal world we have friends, counsellors, psychotherapists, hypnotherapists, NLP practitioners, life coaches, spiritual guides and self-help manuals, each with their own particular formula or method for the attainment of a safe and harmonious internal world. The *Safe Space* procedure uses a combination of these formulas, at the heart of which lies a simple stand alone model based on the idea of *sub-personalities* or semi-autonomous *selves.*

Safe and unsafe space

To describe what a safe place is, independent of context, means very little that is specific, especially since it can be influenced by so many factors, many of which may be outside our sphere of influence.

So, for the sake of this short introduction, let's simplify and say that you occupy a safe space if: a.) You recognise the boundaries of your own personal space, rendering it separate from other spaces. b.) You have control over who crosses your boundaries. c.) You recognize that your

[2] *"A semi-permanent and semi-autonomous region of the personality capable of acting as a person"* - J Rowan *" Patterns of feelings, thoughts, behaviours, perceptions, postures and ways of moving which tend to coalesce in response to various recurring situations in life"* - M. Brown 1979

personal space exists as separate from, but part of a larger space to which you belong or are connected to in some way, which you feel you have the power to contribute to and influence, and which allows for your basic physical, emotional and spiritual needs to be met.

Using the above definition, an *unsafe space* would be a space for which one or more of the above requirements are not met. For example, if we are uncertain about where the boundaries of our space are, we would be less able to protect them and therefore more likely to experience anxiety and panic. In the story of *Sam* this could have meant Sam forgetting the time of the interview.

Safe space experienced as unsafe space

A space does not have to be unsafe for a person to feel unsafe within it. Sometimes our rational conscious mind perceives the space we inhabit to be safe while our instinctive unconscious mind perceives it as being under threat. This conflict often arises when the presenting situation contains elements that, at some level, we associate with a past traumatic experience.

In these instances, our instinct "barks" in much the same way as a guard dog barks in response to combination of sounds, smells, movements, tastes, images and textures that the conscious mind may not notice. This ability of the unconscious mind to connect to details of past events is not surprising when we consider that our unconscious mind is understood to store every single memory, smell, image, taste and event we have ever experienced. Take the story of Sam, for example. Let's fill it in with some history and include that Sam, at the tender age of seven, was humiliated by a teacher in front of the class after failing to recite the seven times table. To punish Sam, or perhaps inspire him, the teacher made him wear a badge with the number seven on it. The feelings of humiliation this younger Sam experienced may have been triggered by a number of similar circumstances mirrored in the interview scenario. For example, the name tag he was required to wear at the interview corresponded with the number seven badge. The other candidates corresponded to his class peers. The speech he had memorised corresponded to his memorising of the seven times table. The interviewer with the power to judge Sam corresponded to the teacher.

Sam's instincts would have picked up on the similarities and warned Sam of the potential impending humiliation.

Sam's conscious mind may not recollect the *originating event* in the classroom, but his unconscious would have triggered feelings of dread. In other words, the presenting circumstances (the name-tag, the peer group, the memory test and the "judge") connected Sam to the feelings of humiliation experienced by a more vulnerable and younger self. Sam's instincts and intuition alerted him to this potential humiliation prompting Sam to throw up defence strategies that culminated in him almost avoiding the interview altogether. These defence strategies may be successful in the short term, but if Sam were to persist in avoiding interviews, he would be unlikely to get another job.

Of course, Sam is no longer a child at school. He has grown and matured into an adult. Sam's instincts, however, may not take this into account. Not, at least, if the dominant feelings and needs are those associated with Sam at the age of seven. Only when Sam's instincts trust that another more resourceful *self* is present to manage the situation will they relax.

In these instances of anxiety and panic, Sam's instinctive *self* is not his enemy, although it may seem like it. On the contrary, it acts with Sam's best interests at heart because it believes that the *self* most dominant at the time is unable to protect Sam. This does not mean that Sam's instinctive *self* knows what to do. It does not know what to do any more than Sam's younger *self* knows. But it can and will throw up defences to protect Sam whether the prevailing circumstances pose a real threat or not.

These defensive strategies often become second nature to us and ingrain themselves into our *personality* to such an extent that they appear to "take over" the personality. We become shy or talkative people, aggressive or manipulative people, pessimistic or over-optimistic people, cynical or naive people. All these behaviours are defences we have at our disposal to dispel or avoid threats, whether real or perceived.

Hypnotherapy & Psychotherapy

Hypnotherapy

Traditionally, one way a hypnotherapist can intervene to change the way our unconscious responds is by using direct or indirect suggestion while the person is in a state of trance. Additionally, the most suitable regression and uncovering techniques may be employed to shift the person's relationship to their experience of the initial trauma or cause. This may include re-experiencing the event using knowledge and skills that were unavailable at the time of the original event. Another techniques used by hypnotherapists is the progressive-retrogressive technique in which the person experiences the event as if they had already overcome their anxiety. Reframing techniques can also be employed to enable the person to view the event from another often more distant, detached or humorous perspective. Anchoring techniques in which desired emotions and feelings can be *triggered* to substitute unwanted ones is another popular and powerful tool. The hypnotherapists Charles Tebbit, John Bradshaw and Roy Hunter also used *Parts therapy* to facilitate dialogue between the conflicting *parts* of the individual so that negotiation can take place and a compromise or agreement reached.

Many of the above interventions and techniques are also used by NLP practitioners. *Safe Space* draws on these techniques and fixes them within the framework of a coherent stand alone therapeutic model specific to anxiety and panic. Incorporated into the procedure is also a person-centred cognitive process in which the client explores and develops their own healing process.

Psychotherapy

Talking therapies, in which I include counselling and psychotherapy, already have their own models upon which to base their interventions. The models provide frameworks around which the therapist navigates in order to assist the client to heal themselves. These models or conceptual systems all bring in the idea of *selves* or sub-personalities in one form or other, using different terms and different ways to describe them. Psychoanalysis has its *id*, *ego* and *superego*. Gestalt therapy uses the concepts of the righteous and authoritarian *Top dog* and the defensive, wheedling *Underdog*. Transactional Analysis talks in terms of *experimental-behavioural* realities, *archeopsychic ego states* or *subselves* all based on the idea of an internal parent, adult and child, for example, the *nurturing parent*, *controlling parent*, *natural child*, *adapted child* and *rebellious child*. The clinical psychologists John and Helen Watkins work with *ego states*, a psychodynamic approach in which techniques of group and family therapy are employed to resolve conflicts between various *ego states* that constitute a *family of self* or *confederation of component segments*. Psychosynthesis aims at the *integration of elements* or *semi-autonomous subpersonalities*, of which a whole host have been named including the *Hag*, *Mystic*, *Materialist*, *Idealist*, *Claw*, *Pillar of Strength*, *Sneak*, and many more. Psychodrama uses the *Multiple Double Technique* in which the person is on the stage with several doubles of himself, all of which are acted out by the protagonist at some point, prompting dialogue between the *doubles*. Voice Dialogue refers to sub personalities as *energy patterns* which are identified as *the protector/controller, the publisher, the critic, the perfectionist, the power brokers, the pleaser, the inner child, the good and bad mother, and the good and bad father.* Voice dialogue, as with Gestalt therapy uses empty chairs or cushions to encourage the person to come to terms with the sub-personality in question, encouraging an *Aware Ego* to take responsibility for the dance of the sub personalities.

Whatever the approach and whatever terms are employed, all draw upon a concept of *sub personalities* or *selves.* This book does not attempt to modify or re-define these approaches. It draws on aspects of their respective frameworks in order to identify a simplified model that is applicable and specific to the treatment of anxiety and panic. It hopes to do this in a way that is accessible to individuals with no prior knowledge of hypnotherapy or psychotherapy. *Chapter 2* of this book defines the *selves* used in the *Safe Space Model.*

I have employed the term *selves,* as opposed to *sub-personalities* or *parts,* because in my opinion it is more colloquial than *sub-personalities* and conveys the idea of them having a semi-autonomous nature better than the term *part.*

The *Safe Space* model

The *core selves*

The *Safe Space Model* is made up of three *core selves*: ***The Parent self, Child self*** and ***Protector.*** These *core selves* have the following *core* needs, resources and responsibilities.

Parent (female)	nurturing, listening, comforting, forgiveness,
Parent (male)	instructing, focusing, perseverance, consistency
Child	playing, laughing, crying, exploring, receiving
Protector	intuition, instinct, sounding alarm, attacking, defending, avoiding, seducing

Defining a *self* can include personifying it by endowing it with a name, gender, age, body, voice, and any additional qualities, resources and needs. For example, the *Protector* could be a man that shouts, a woman that screams, a lion that growls, a rooster that crows, a goose that honks, a dog that barks, a mythological creature that breathes fire.

The terms *male* and *female* do not refer to the gender but rather to the quality and characteristics of the *self.* Thus the *male parent* could be represented as a female and vice versa. Each *self* is specific to an experience, not the person. Each self's age, characteristics, needs and responsibilities are those that relate to the experience and can therefore change over time. The following *Family Analogy* illustrates the model and how it works.

The Family Analogy

In the *Family Analogy,* the *parent female self* is represented by the *mother*, the *parent male self* by the *father*, the *child self* by the *son* or *daughter* and the *Protector* by the *pet dog.*

As with most families, although the roles of the family members are not fixed, there are certain characteristics, responsibilities and needs that are generally associated with each member. For example, we can say that the mother's and father's responsibilities include providing a safe and nurturing environment in which the child can grow, play, explore and learn. We can say that the dog's role includes alerting the family when someone is at the door. We can say that it is okay for the dog to bark aggressively at threatening strangers, but not okay for it to bark aggressively at the family members, especially the child.

Some roles are interchangeable, while others are not. For example, the mother and father can, independently or together, answer the door, earn money, change nappies, do the washing up, make decisions about which house to buy or what colour to paint the walls. The child is not responsible for providing food for the parents, though he or she might have a say in what food is bought. The pet dog is certainly not responsible for cooking!

Certain roles, then, are associated with certain family members, which are associated with certain needs and responsibilities. And for the family to feel safe and "united", all the family members must be present to fulfil their roles and responsibilities. The following two stories illustrate what can happen when all the family members are present and co-operative, and what can happen when they are not.

Safe Family Analogy

The Jones family live in a two-storey house in the suburbs. Ruth is in the sitting room watching TV. James, her husband, is in the kitchen washing up. Lolita, their seven year old daughter, is upstairs playing with her dolls. The family pet dog, Woof, is curled up on the sofa next to Ruth.

There are three knocks on the door. Woof pricks up his ears and gives a little bark.

"I'll get it!" calls James from the kitchen.

Ruth strokes Woof soothingly. "Calm down, Woof," she says. Woof calms down, but keeps his ears pricked, attentive to the sound of James' footsteps as he moves towards the front door. The door opens. A conversation ensues that gets progressively louder until shouting can be heard. Woof jumps up and runs to the door, followed by Ruth. At the top of the stairs Lolita's head peers around the banister. She is disturbed by the argument taking place at the front door. Ruth goes to comfort and protect her daughter while James and Woof finally repel the unwelcome guest. They succeed. The door closes and everyone returns to what they were doing.

Unsafe Family Analogy

The Jones family are doing the same things at the same time, but on a different day. James finishes the washing up and decides to do some DIY in the shed at the end of the garden. "I'm off to the shed," he calls to Ruth as he leaves through the back door. But Ruth is half way through the front door to get something from her neighbour. "I'm just popping next door," she calls. Neither hears one another.

A few minutes later there are three knocks on the front door. Woof pricks up his ears and gives a little bark. There is no response. Woof barks louder. There are more, louder knocks on the door. *Knock! Knock! Knock!* Woof jumps up and runs to the front door. *Woof Woof Woof*, he barks. At the top of the stairs Lolita's head peers around the banister. The scene disturbs her and she calls out for mummy and daddy. There is no reply. Lolita doesn't know what to do and starts crying which makes Woof bark even louder, prompting Lolita to cry louder still until finally, in a state of panic, she runs to her parents' bedroom and hides under the bed.

Lolita's parents eventually return at the same time and are confronted with a barking dog and a child crying under their bed. Whoever was at the front door has gone.

The essential difference between the two stories is that in the *Safe Family Analogy* the parents were present to deal with the potential threat, and in the *Unsafe Family Analogy* they were not. In this second analogy, how the mother and father subsequently respond to the barking dog and the child crying under the bed will depend on their individual resources, needs and characteristics. The father, for example, may try to calm the dog using either a command or a soothing gesture. The mother may try to comfort the child with a hug, a lullaby or an explanation. All are responses and reactions to the fact that the parents were absent at the time of the perceived threat.

Although the dog warned off the potential danger, it is not the dog's role to protect the child, but merely to inform the adults of the potential danger and act as back-up if needed. If the parents are not present, the dog's barking, instead of calming the child, makes the child feel more anxious.

If we add to the end of this scene a traumatic consequence such as someone breaking into the house, kicking the dog and ransacking the house, the experience may become an *originating event* and the feelings associated with the memory of it may be triggered by similar circumstances in the future. These triggers could include the sound of three knocks on a door, the sound of a dog barking, the colour of the intruder's coat, dolls similar to the ones Lolita was playing with, or any combination of sounds, textures, movements, images and tastes the child experienced.

When we think of these family members in terms of our *internal family of selves*, the experience of having absent internal parents is that of not having the physical, mental, intellectual or emotional resources to protect a vulnerable *self* (or collection of feelings and needs) from a particular perceived threat.

If this absenteeism of the *parent self* is frequent, or the individual has not acquired the necessary resources to protect themselves, the *child self* would either learn to hide better or adopt the defence strategies of the *Protector/dog*. Otherwise the child would be completely vulnerable. If this were to continue for a long time, as the child grows, the qualities of the *guard* would be the ones the *child* models themselves upon. This does not necessarily mean that the person learns to be loud, aggressive or to "bark" a lot. A *Protector* can also respond by running or hiding, just as a dog can put its tail between its legs and submit to a "bigger dog".

Safe Space is based on the premise that one of the main causes of anxiety and panic is the experience of having absent or unprepared internal *parent selves* at a time when the person's personal space is being threatened. The

Safe Space procedure that follows aims to reinstate and strengthen these absent internal parents and to train the *protector* to respond appropriately.

The *Safe Space* Procedure

The *Safe Space* procedure consists of 7 *steps*. As a general rule, each step corresponds to a single session. However, as every case is unique, some steps may overlap, their order may change and the time allotted to each may vary. Some steps may be missed out altogether. I usually begin with the following order in mind and, if possible, try to stick to it. Notes on the subject for both practitioners and those using the book as a self-help manual can be found in *Chapter 4: The Procedure.*

Step 1: The Present

Step 1 focuses on the circumstances, symptoms and triggers of your anxiety or panic.

It has *3 parts*. In *part 1* you identify your situation as you see it now, and how you want it to change. In *Part 2* you describe in the form of a *story* the events and circumstances that trigger your anxiety or panic. In *Part 3* you explore reasons why you have been unable or unwilling to overcome your anxiety or panic until now.

Step 2: A Possible Future

Step 2 focuses on how to achieve the change you desire.

There are 2 *parts* to this *step*. *Part 1* provides an analogy that offers a new perspective on your *story* and a means of achieving an alternative ending. *Part 2* uses a *what if* scenario that enables you to visualize what your future might be like were you to overcome your anxiety.

Step 3: The Past

This *step* focuses on the original cause of your anxiety and on the feelings this event prompted. The purpose of this *step* is not to relive the experience, but to lay the groundwork for *step 5* in which you change the way you relate to the experience.

This *step* has *2 parts*. In *Part 1* you identify the event or set of circumstances that lie at the root of your anxiety. In *Part 2* you identify the feelings that you associate with this event.

Step 4: The Internal Family of Selves

In this *step* you identify the needs, desires and resources of your *parent self, child self* and *protector*. The work done in this *step* prepares you for the tasks in *step* 5 in which you change how you feel about the event that originally caused your anxiety

Step 5: Healing the Past

The purpose of this *step* is to heal your relationship with the event that lies at the root of your anxiety so that the feelings you associated with it no longer haunt the present. Entitled, *parenting the child*, it consists of incorporating into the event your *parent self* in order to change the outcome of the event and thus your *child self's* experience of it.

Step 6: Retraining Instincts

This *step* offers a way of training your instincts to respond appropriately to presenting circumstances, and offers a technique that enables you to access positive feelings.

This *step* has 3 *parts.* In *part 1* you "tame" your *protector* so that you control it rather than it control you. In *part 2* you redeploy the skills and resources previously primarily engaged in self-protection. In *part 3* you learn how to access resources and to substitute undesired feelings for desired ones.

Step 7: The Future

The purpose of this *step* is to reinforce and confirm the changes you have made.

This *step* has 4 *Parts. Part 1* is a visualization in which you progress forwards in time to glimpse how your *new self* might experience life. *Part 2* is a visualization technique that substitutes your *old story* for your *new story. Part 3* introduces affirmations as a means of reinforcing your *new beliefs. Part 4* uses "real life" experience to confirm that change has taken place.

2
Model & Theory

What makes a grown up grown up? - The Body - The Emotional self
The Safe Space internal family of selves - The role of mediator

What makes a grown up *grown up*?

For many people, being a *grown up* means being rational and responsible. Irrational fears such as fear of the dark, ghosts, vampires and goblins belong to the domain of childhood. Yet acute anxiety and panic are often perceived and experienced as irrational, debilitating fears, which often develop in adulthood and can grow more intense with age. What differentiates, then, a child from a *grown up*? Naturally, to become a *grown up* we must all first pass through being a baby, a child and a teenager, or adolescent, the Latin root of which actually means "to grow up".

As teenagers, many of us regarded the expression *grown up* as something to be spat out, rather like a Brussels sprout. We associated becoming a *grown up* with the unsavoury task of having to surrender our own free will to the restrictive boundaries of a monotonous career, a long term relationship and family outings. Something about it all made many of us just want to rebel.

Part of our resistance towards growing up was perhaps due to the fact that it was *grown ups* who were telling us to grow up, and as far as many of us could see, *grown ups* seemed far less equipped than children at being happy and having fun. Another possible reason for our resistance to *growing up* was the implied rule that our emotional age should somehow match our physical age, and that if it did not, we would be out of synch with the natural order of things. In other words, there would be something wrong with us. Given the spotty transition our hormones were subjecting our bodies to as we grew from child to adult, it was hardly surprising that many of us had mixed feelings about growing up. We knew we could not stop our bodies from making the transition, but we would try to hang onto our youthful unpredictability, our fiery free will and the belief that the world would be whatever we wanted it to be.

Naturally, we all experience growing up differently. However, there do seem to be a collection of needs, desires and fears that are common to us all and which we generally associate with different ages or stages of development. For example, it is often deemed quite normal for a child aged three to nine to say words to the effect of, *I want! Give me! Give me! It's mine!* From a mature adult, on the other hand, we may expect something more along the lines of, *Yes, I want it but I am prepared to share it, and if you really need it I will give it to you.* Most adults, though, feel prompted at some time or other to say both.

More often than not, the first of these standpoints we consider to be childish or immature, and the second to be mature. Likewise, the being selfish, self-centred and possessive are often associated with immaturity, while selflessness, compassion and the ability to focus on the bigger picture are often associated with maturity. Naturally, children may happily give up their favourite Action man or Barbie for the greater good of Mankind, but they are more likely to want to hang onto them. But then again, as mature *grown ups*, we may be more ready to contemplate the bigger picture, and often want to, but we certainly never lose touch of our own personal picture, prompting us to cling on to whatever possessions and beliefs we can. Most adults, in fact, can swing from being self-centred to selfless and back again within the space of a few minutes. Adolescents sometimes appear to achieve being both at the same time!

Whatever our age, then, we all have the ability to be immature or mature, childish and adult. In the privacy of our homes, for example, we may sometimes feel like having a pillow fight and leaving the feathers to blow themselves away, while at other times we prohibit messy games. When we turn on the television, there are times when we feel like watching a soap opera and times when we are drawn towards a documentary. When playing a game, there are occasions when we graciously accept defeat and congratulate our victor, and occasions when we embark on a temper tantrum, blame bad luck and accuse our opponent of foul play. At work, we may one day laugh at a practical joke played on a colleague, and the next day raise a disapproving eyebrow. While helping someone out, we all have the ability to be encouraging and patient, yet we can all be critical and impatient and punitive. Two hours before an important meeting, we may feel anxious and panicky, yet two minutes before a potentially suicidal fare ground ride we may feel excited and exhilarated. In other words, we can all be irresponsible and responsible, intuitive and calculating, controlling and submissive, gracious and ungracious, selfish and selfless, possessive and generous, playful and serious, amoral and compassionate, aggressive and passive. We all yearn to belong and we all crave to break free. We can all be childish and we can all behave like adults.

This ability to feel and respond in such a variety of ways not only makes for a more varied and fulfilling life, but is also necessary because different situations require different responses, skills and resources. There would be little point in playing a competitive sport, for example, if we could not draw on the competitive side of our nature. Nor would we be very good parents or teachers if we had not acquired the necessary patience and compassion to deal with a learner's frustrations.

One way of understanding why apparently irrational anxious and panicky feelings seem to debilitate us is to see them as the consequence of a particular *self* not having its needs met and thus dominating our experience to such an extent that the skills and resources of other *selves* cannot be accessed.

Someone who is *not* suffering from debilitating anxiety and panic could, then, be defined as someone not having any one particular *self* or set of needs dominate their experience and therefore able to access all their resources and skills. This integrated state in which a person has all their needs met and is able to access all their inner resources is referred to in this book as being *grown up*. Usually this *grown up* benefits from the stability and of a nurturing group or set of beliefs and a strong, independent individual identity. It is someone who belongs and who is free.

Being a *grown up* is not something we *are* or *are not*. Rather, it is a state we experience from time to time to varying degrees. Though we may never be able to maintain this balanced *grown up* state for any lengthy continuous period of time, to help enable us achieve it more often it is useful to know what our needs, desires, fears and resources are, and to find a way to manage them. One way of doing this is by personifying them, as if they were different parts of ourselves. These "little people inside us" are sometimes referred to as sub-personalities, and in this book they are referred to as *selves*. Whether or not we are actually composed of different sub-personalities or *selves* does not really matter. It is merely a conceptual system that allows us to understand and manage our internal world.

At the heart of the *Safe Space* is the idea that someone is less likely to experience feelings of anxiety and panic if the needs of their internal *selves* are catered for, and whose resources and skills can be accessed at any time.

To help enable us to define these *selves*, it is useful to first understand where they came from, and to do that we must understand how a person develops over time, both as a physical being and as an emotional one.

The Body

As people, the easiest *self* to define is the body - our physical self. Regardless of race, status or wealth, our body is born and dies. Separating these two events is the body's life span during which time it constantly changes. It gets taller, fatter, thinner, heavier, lighter, stronger, weaker and older. Some of these changes we can control to varying degrees. For instance, we can control how strong or weak our body is by exercising it or not. Other changes we can influence but not control, for example, we can extend or shorten our body's lifespan by altering how we nurture, feed, rest and protect it. Other changes are forced upon us, like the process of aging. We may be able to make ourselves appear older or younger, but we cannot slow time down or speed it up, reverse it or stop it. Whether we want to get older or not, our body's birthdays come along, one after the other, at exactly the same time as it takes the earth to complete its orbit around the sun.

As with earth years, everything about our physical body we can measure precisely, enabling us to give each body a unique identity that both differentiates it from and connects it to other bodies. For example, Sam, on the day I first met him, was a thirty-eight year old white Caucasian male weighing around seventy-six kilos and measuring about five foot eleven inches. He had mousy hair, brown eyes and pale skin.

In the unlikely event that I had at my disposal every measuring device available, I would be able to precisely determine every physical characteristic of Sam's body, with the exception of his age. Some people don't even know their own age, especially in countries where birth certificates are not always issued. Naturally, there are tell-tail signs such as size, posture and skin texture. Certainly Sam as a foetus looked nothing like Sam as a mature adult. On the other hand, Sam at the age of thirty-eight would look pretty much like Sam at the age of thirty-nine.

There are, however, certain physical developments that occur in the same particular order for everyone, even if the precise age at which they occur differs for each person. The physical developments of Sam's body went as follows.

Sam's physical development

At conception the sperm of Sam's father-to-be and the ovum of his mother-to-be fused together to form a zygote – Sam's first cell. The zygote then divided and multiplied until it developed into an embryo which lived, fed and grew inside his mother's uterus. A few weeks later the embryo was called a foetus and developed male organs. Seven months later Sam the baby boy was born, he took his first breath and the umbilical chord that connected him to his mother was severed. This moment is considered by many cultures to be the beginning of Sam's life as a person.[3]

For the first one and a half years Sam was called an *infant* or *baby* and was completely dependent on his mother[4] for food and protection. By the time he reached the age of one and a half he had grown about three times bigger and was referred to as a *toddler*. He was still dependent on adults for food and protection. At the age of four, Sam's body became a bigger, stronger *prepubescent* and continued to grow steadily through early and middle childhood until he reached *puberty* and *adolescence* at around the age of thirteen. His voice broke, body hair began to grow, he noticeably shot up in height and he began to produce sperm, thus becoming fertile and able to start the whole process off again.

After a few years of this hormonal avalanche Sam was referred to as a *young adult* and a few years later, an *adult*. His body ticked over pretty smoothly after that, at least until when Sam reached the age of thirty-eight when I had the privilege of working with him. As far as Sam's future is concerned, bar any major accidents or illnesses, I could assume that Sam's body would reach *middle adulthood* and beyond, that his hair would start to thin and turn grey, that muscles and joints would lose some of their flexibility, bone mass would decrease, energy levels diminish and senses become less acute. At some point Sam would also lose his ability to pro-create, and some

---

[3] I respectfully acknowledge those who believe that human life begins at conception.

[4] Competent adult

time after that, later rather than sooner I hope, Sam's body would take its last breath and die.

Jeanette's physical development

For females, some of the physical developments are different and often occur at slightly different ages, but the process and order remain the same. The physical development of Sam's sister, Jeanette, differed in the following ways. The foetus developed female organs. She reached adolescence and puberty slightly earlier than Sam. This was accompanied by the beginning of menstruation when the first of a finite number of eggs was released, breast growth, and an increase in pelvic width and in the amount of subcutaneous fat. Middle age for Jeanette will probably not be accompanied by as much hair loss but her ability to procreate may well cease sooner when she releases the last of her eggs, thus heralding the end of her menstrual cycle and the beginning of menopause. Like Sam's body, Jeanette's would die, though statistically she has more chance of living longer.

Fortunately for Sam and Jeanette, and for the rest of us, in order to put off this inevitable demise for as long as possible, the body has at its disposal several highly effective protective mechanisms. Its skin shields it from harmful ultraviolet light, bacteria, parasites and, to some extent, hard objects such as stones and nails. Its immune system fights against substances that do manage to gain entry and against cancerous cells that develop spontaneously in the body. The body's nervous system makes possible the kind of learning it needs to cope with changes in the environment. Its senses detect danger, and the hormone system stimulates the heart and gains access to increased energy levels in preparation for the fight or flight response. Finally, its reproductive system ensures the continuation of its line and the species. All in all, the body is pretty well equipped at looking after itself.

Although the order of the body's development and how it protects itself are the same regardless of culture, gender and race, different societies place different meaning and importance on developmental stages and on the transition from one to the other. In the West, for example, puberty (the maturation of the body in preparation for reproduction) occurs several years before an age generally considered physically and psychologically appropriate for parenthood and sexual relations. It is, in fact, a punishable crime in most countries to have sexual intercourse under the age of sixteen.

One of the reasons why underage sex is considered inappropriate is the belief that while our physical selves are, to some degree, prepared for procreation, our emotional, intellectual and social selves are not. In other words, the emotional self that inhabits the physical self has its own independent developmental stages and protective mechanisms which do not necessarily develop in synch with those of the body's.

The Emotional self

The *emotional self*, though irrevocably linked to the body, is more difficult to define. There is no equivalent system of calendar years, kilos and centimetres to measure it by. We cannot see, touch, taste, smell or hear it. What we can do is associate each developmental stage with the development of certain needs, desires, fears, skills and resources; the developmental rates of which seem to be determined and influenced by both the genes we inherit and by the environment we grow up in.

Sam's emotional, intellectual and social development went something like this. Much of it taken from Sam's diary, some has been deduced and the odd bits invented. Nevertheless, it is a feasible and unexceptional story.

Sam's emotional, intellectual and social development

When Sam was a baby he was helpless and completely dependent on his mother for his survival. He needed maximum comfort with minimal uncertainty, the abundance or lack of which would influence his propensity to trust or mistrust in the external world. Fortunately for Sam, he was fed regularly, he was not abandoned for any lengthy periods of time and did not experience any major prolonged discomfort. His trust in the external world got off to a good start.

By the time he was a six month old baby, he could smile, babble, enjoyed being cuddled and could distinguish his mother from other people. He responded to his own name and began to expect things like being fed and dressed. After nine months, he could crawl, he laughed and got distressed when separated from his mother. Aged one, he could stand, give and take objects, he could say *yes* and *no* and understood what they meant. He responded to simple commands like *Stop it!* He felt affection towards people he knew, feared people he didn't, and experienced anger for the first time. The world, in other words, changed from being a single amorphous extension of himself to something populated by independent beings with lives of their own. Sam became curious about this world and began to explore it.

When he became a *toddler* at the age of one and a half, he could walk, creep up the stairs and draw a reasonably straight line with a crayon. He still got upset when separated from his mother and feared having a bath. He could repeat a few words, feed himself and became interested in his mirror image. In his attempt to master the world, he learned what he could and couldn't control, developed a sense of free will and a corresponding sense of regret, sorrow, pride, shame and doubt, all of which were influenced by the responses he received from the external world, in particular his parents. The foundations of his self-esteem were being laid.

By the age of two he could run, kick a ball and build a tower with six cubes. He could control his bowels and bladder and say more than two hundred words. He slept half as much as he had previously, had temper tantrums, resented his new born sister and did pretty much the opposite of what he was told.

Aged three, he became a *prepubescent preschooler* and learned to ride a tricycle, string together sentences and initiate activities. He developed a conscience, an imagination and a sexual identity, along with which came pleasure, guilt and remorse. He still feared being separated from his mother, became violently emotional, began to stutter briefly and developed a sense of humour. He learned to distinguish between *I* and *me*. He became clingy and dependent, was possessive about his toys, yet loved playing alongside other children. Although he still copied his parent's actions, he resisted his parent's demands and gave his own orders, one of these being the insistence that his routines remained the same.

By the age of four, he could stand on one leg, draw a circle and was self sufficient in many routines of home life like brushing his teeth and combing his hair. Although he was affectionate towards his parents, his new found independence was accompanied by an embarrassment in public of being with them. He would not, for example, let his mother brush his hair in view of others, he resisted having his hand held and he would certainly not divulge his new found pleasure in genital manipulation. He became intensely interested in other children's bodies, had a romantic attachment to his mother and became jealous of his father. He also became afraid of the dark for the first time. The word *we* entered his vocabulary, he learned to play with other children as opposed to alongside them, and he had an *imaginary friend* who accompanied him constantly.

By the age of five, he could dress himself, had mastered grammar and knew over two thousand words. He became responsible for things like getting up, and experienced guilt or pride depending on whether or not he accomplished his task. He would rather play with other children than adults, became highly competitive and preferred football to skipping and Action Man to Barbie. He also marched arm in arm in the school playground with his male friends singing "Who wants to play war - no girls!"

As a seven year old *prepubescent* Sam really began to have a sense of himself as a separate autonomous individual. He started to compare himself to others and tried to do things well and correctly, refining his skills and developing a sense of worth which identified him with feelings of superiority and inferiority. His main skill was running fast. He also made his first *real friend*, as opposed to *imaginary one*. It was at this time that his parents divorced and that he experienced acute humiliation in front of his classmates when he was unable to recite the seven times table.

As Sam grew into an *adolescent* he battled to form both a social identity as a member of a group, and a personal identity as an independent individual with unique thoughts, desires, abilities and goals. This meant experimenting with different styles of clothes and hair cuts as he attempted to integrate his roles as child, brother, boyfriend, student, athlete, friend, intellect and artist into a unique, identifiable individual, all the while under the influence of peer group and role model pressure. He also "fell in love" for the first time and felt the pain of separation and loss which accompanied being "dumped".

When Sam became a *young adult*, in an attempt to embrace intimacy and ward off isolation, he began to learn to give and receive love and to make personal commitments in a way that took the needs of others into consideration. He lived alone for the first

> time and co-habited with a girlfriend for the first time. As he got older he sought satisfaction through work, governed by a need to enhance creativity, ward of stagnation and gain recognition, love, respect and admiration. He also began, albeit unconsciously, his search for the right person to have a family with.
>
> When Sam decided to overcome his anxiety and panic, his life as an *older adult* had yet to transpire. Were he to survive another forty years, however, he would possibly develop a sense of acceptance of life as he had lived it and would learn to recognise and appreciate more the importance of the people and relationships that he had developed over his lifetime. He would likely review his life's accomplishments with some ambiguity. He may develop an interest in guiding the development of the next generation, and would be obliged to learn to deal with loss and prepare himself for death. His body would then die and his spirit, soul or essence would either migrate somewhere else or be confined to the memory of others.

Although Sam's personal circumstances are unique, most of his learning, needs, fears and desires are ones that we have all evolved and experienced at some time in our lives.

Unlike the physical body, which goes through the same developmental process largely regardless of personal circumstances, the *emotional self* seems to be influenced to a greater degree by experience. Certainly, how we feel about and react to events in the present is influenced by past experience. For example, the fact that Sam at the age of thirty-eight felt anxious and panicky in situations during which he felt he could be judged and publicly humiliated was likely influenced by his humiliating experience at the age of seven when he was unable to recite the seven times table in front of his class. Likewise, the mistrust Sam revealed he harboured towards his romantic attachments to woman became easier to understand and overcome once he had divulged that his mother had been repeatedly unfaithful to his father.

Both the humiliation that Sam experienced in the classroom and the manner in which his parents separated were outside of Sam's sphere of influence at the time they occurred. In other words, his emotional development as a child was something Sam could not control completely and was something therefore that he was not entirely responsible for. Either Sam did not have the resources and experience to influence the events, or the events were determined by other people such as parents, the teacher, God or fate if you believe in them, or the amoral randomness of nature. Whatever the case, the events "happened to" Sam, directly or indirectly. His parents divorced each other, and the maths teacher's authority enabled him, deliberately or not, to undermine Sam's confidence and self-esteem.

Just as no child can control or determine the circumstances that mould their emotional development, nor can any adult alter the past and change what "happened to" them. It is possible, however, to change our relationship to past events and by doing so disempowering them of their negative and restrictive influences on the present. Whether we choose to do this or not is something that we determine ourselves and are therefore responsible for. For this change in relationship to occur, the *Safe Space* procedure requires that we define those *aspects* of ourselves that we are going to employ to make this change possible, referred to here as the *Safe Space family of selves.*

The *Safe Space* internal family of selves

We know through experience that the *emotional self* is made up of a myriad of often conflicting needs, fears and desires that we can associate with different ages or stages of development, and that these needs, fears and desires remain with us throughout our lives. Regardless of our physical age, our *emotional self* can be needy and clingy in a child-like way, harbour desires to rebel in an adolescent-like way, and be forgiving and self-sacrificing in a mature, adult-like way. In other words, it can regress, progress and remain the same.

We also know that, although we always have an element of control over how we behave, how we respond is often influenced by past experiences. Combinations of sounds, smells, images, tastes and textures all trigger memories and feelings that change our mood. For example, a song on the radio that we once played while pining for a lost love may prompt us to feel sad and melancholy; the smell of freshly cut grass may make us hark back to the playing fields of our youth; the scent of a familiar aftershave or perfume may arouse our desires; someone suddenly raising a hand may cause us to flinch, if another hand raised in a similar fashion had once ended up bruising our face; words said with a particular tone may prompt us to be mistrustful, if a similar tone had once been used to shroud lies; a particular phone ring may startle us, if the same tone had once preceded particularly bad news. Even the tiniest, faintest stimuli in our environment can throw up needs, desires and fears that often have nothing to do with the present circumstances. Often these triggers are so subtle or embedded in our unconscious that we are completely unaware of them, and thus at a complete loss as to explain our mood swings. Sometimes these mood swings, especially those that create anxiety and panic, prompt us to behave in ways that are not always in our best interests. For example, Sam's desire to run away from interviews and sabotage relationships with loving partners certainly did not help him feel good about himself or provide him with what he ideally really wanted.

To summarise, how we respond to certain situations and people often depends on which needs and desires are dominant at the time, which are influenced by and sometimes determined by stimuli that connect the present circumstances to past experiences. Sometimes we are aware of these stimuli, other times we are not. Sometimes our mood changes so abruptly that it is as if we turn into another person, hence the expression, *I don't feel myself,* and the reproach, *I don't feel I know who you are any more!* These different "people inside us" or *selves* that "pop up" or "take over" often do so unexpectedly and other times predictably. As explained in chapter one, the *Safe Space internal family of selves* distinguishes between three different *selves* or *internal family members*: The *parent self*, the *child self* and the *protector*, each of which is associated with a collection of needs, fears, desires and resources.

The *parent self* & the *child self*

A premise of *Safe Space* model and procedure is that an individual is less likely to experience anxiety and panic when the needs and desires of their *internal family of selves* are all catered for. Thus, an individual is more likely to experience anxiety or panic when the needs of a given *self* are not met, prompting those needs and desires to dominate the individual's experience. For those who experience acute anxiety and panic it is often the needs and fears associated with the *child self* that dominate our experience. Or, put another way, it is the absence of the resources and skills of a sufficiently evolved *parent self*.

To manage, evolve and maintain some semblance of control over the relationship between these *selves* or *internal family members*, we must first define what their individual needs, fears, desires and resources are. Although every individual *self* is unique, just as each individual is unique, the *Safe Space* model identifies certain *core qualities* that seem to exist for all *child selves* and *parent selves*. Sam is no exception.

Sam had his own way of referring and talking about his *internal family of* selves, which he called his *collection of little heads and hearts.* Personally I like Sam's definition. A more academic minded person might prefer the following definition: a semi-autonomous collection of needs, desires, memories, experiences, resources and patterns of behaviour that coalesce to form a personality that is capable of acting autonomously to various situations in life.

Sam's *parent self* and *child self*

Sam's *parent self* he called the *Careful Sage.* His *child self he* referred to as the *carefree explorer.* Sam associated them with the following characteristics. They are, in my experience, archetypal qualities of the *parent self* and the *child self.*

Sam's *parent Self*		Sam's *child self*
Male	**Female**	
Role Being responsible for child self	**Role** Being responsible for child self	**Role** To play and have fun
Character Controlling	**Character** Nurturing	**Character** Spontaneously emotional
Needs To be respected	**Needs** To have something to nurture	**Needs** To feel safe, loved and stimulated
Resources Focused, determined, logical, pro-active, directive, rigid, forward thinking	**Resources** Compassionate, understanding, tolerant, patient, good listener, pacifying, forgiving	**Resources:** Intuitive, curious, able to live in the here and now
Tools Punishments and treats.	**Tools** Communication and hugs.	**Tools** Imagination

To help Sam identify with these two *selves*, he characterized them by giving each one an age and physical characteristics. Although Sam's physical appearance did not actually alter when the needs or desires of a particular *self* dominated, it was always fairly clear which *self* was more demanding of attention because each had his or her own particular way of moving and speaking. For example, when the needs and desires of Sam's *child self* were dominant, Sam would often fidget, his voice would have a slightly higher pitch and he would be more animated and spontaneous. When Sam's *parent self* was dominant, he would often cross his legs and his expressions would be more controlled.

Anxiety caused by a "needy" *child self*

An excellent example of how the domination of the needs and desires associated to one self over those of another can lead to anxiety and panic, was given to me by Sam. The example relates to an internal conflict he experienced between his *careless adventurer (child self)* and his *careful sage (parent self)* when planning a long awaited holiday. The conflict, in which the needs and desires of Sam's *child self* dominated those of his *parent self*, exemplifies how the absence of a sufficiently evolved *parent self* can lead to anxiety and panic.

The following extract is taken from Sam's *journal* and, it seems, was written predominantly by his *child self* who Sam refers to as his *Carefree explorer*.

> **Sam's journal: My holiday drama**
>
> I have often lain awake at night dreaming of grabbing my rucksack, leaving the washing up in the sink and heading of towards the unbeaten paths of the African plain. No map, no compass, no phone. Just me and nature. Life, after all, is an adventure and the more you risk the more you gain. So when I finally managed to arrange some time off work, my impulse was to do just that. I would live my dream.
>
> Somewhere at the back of my mind, however, a nagging, tiresome little voice kept telling me not to be so rash. *Wouldn't it be better*, the voice suggested, *to just advance book yourself into a nice little hotel with an ocean view and a pool-side bar. Life is hard enough as it is. You need to rest and unwind. You need to let go.*

As if I would! I could just imagine myself sitting by the pool and drowning Sahara cocktails next to Bob the builder. No way! I began to pack my rucksack: sunglasses, cash, T-shirts, turban.

What about a map and compass? the little annoying voice butted in. *If you are heading off into the wild, you need to be prepared. You could die out there!*

That's the whole point! I replied defiantly. To feel alive, you have to brush with death.

And I did. In the middle of a sand storm, parched, starving, burnt, lost and alone, I thought, *Oh my god, why didn't I bring a water bottle, emergency rations and some company!* And I panicked.

When Sam was planning his holiday, it was clearly the needs and desires of his *carefree explorer self* or *child self* that dominated, and when he found himself lost and alone, the same *child self* panicked.

This inability to control which needs, desires and resources determine our actions can make for some pretty uncomfortable situations, especially if the needs of the *child self* completely ignore the resources and experience of the *parent self*. This is equally true the other way around. For example, if Sam had only heeded the advice of his *Careful sage self*, he may have found himself tearing his hair out with boredom on a poolside sun lounger next to Bob the builder, wishing he were wrapped in a turban and lost in some desert wasteland.

Ideally, of course, the two *selves* would take each other into consideration at the planning stage, thus benefiting from one another's skills and resources. The *Carefree explorer* could then happily wander off into the unknown, safe in the knowledge that the *Careful sage* had planned with sufficient foresight to ensure that potential problems did not turn into anxiety provoking crises. For example, his *Careful sage self (parent self)* would have ensured that the necessary bookings were made, that alternative routes had been studied, itineraries organised, that the necessary safety precautions were in place and that the needs and desires of other people involved in the trip would be taken into consideration. The *child self* would have ensured that there were enough unpredictable ingredients to make the trip a "real" adventure. In other words, the trip would be exciting and spontaneous, yet planned sufficiently to cater for any disasters.

Getting exactly the right balance is, of course, almost impossible as it necessitates being a perfectly balanced individual which, in my experience, does not exist, at least not for any prolonged period of time. Sam isn't always perfectly balanced, and never will be. Invariably, one or other *self* is either partially dominant or absent, sulking, rebellious, uninterested or overwhelmed. Somehow the consistently happy *internal family of selves* seems to elude us all. With time, Sam did manage to partially readdress the balance of his internal world by evolving and acknowledging the importance of his *parent self*.

So, when we become anxious or panicky, it could be because the needs and desires of a particular *self* dominate our experience of an event. It is often the needs of *child self* that dominate to such an extent that skills and resources of the *parent self* cannot be accessed.

In the example of Sam wanting to run away from his interview, he may have wished to tap into the resources, skills and experience of his *parent self*, but for some reason he was unable. And once we become entrenched in a particular state of mind or "dominated" by a particular *self*, it is often difficult to "snap out of it", even when we want to.

Catering for often conflicting needs and desires is made even more difficult when we take into consideration that they are influenced and, to some extent, determined by other people's needs and desires. Not only, then, do we have to overcome our own internal conflict, but must compromise with other potentially more powerful personalities. For example, when accompanied by someone who is particularly authoritarian and controlling, there is a tendency in most of us to want to either relinquish responsibility or to rebel. Likewise, if the person we are with is being particularly irresponsible, there is a tendency to become more authoritarian and responsible. Depending on who we are with, we can demand like children, engage in the happy banter as friends, be jealous lovers, authoritarian fathers, nurturing mothers, annoying brothers and sisters. When we are unable, for whatever reason, to control which *self* is dominant, we are effectively *out of control.* It is this being *out of control* that is often the precursor and sometimes the cause of anxiety and panic.

Fortunately, to compensate for and, to some extent, counter this feeling of being *out of control*, there is another member of the *Safe Space internal family* we can call on. It is a member that works to keep us safe by alerting us to and protecting us from potential threats and suffering. In the *Safe Space* model, this *self* is called the *protector*, and has at its disposal a whole array of protective strategies.

The *protector*

The role of the *protector* is to protect us from potential threats to our safety. It "sniffs out" danger and responds to it instinctively or according to how it has been trained. Like the pet dog *Woof* in the *Family Analogy*, whatever situation we find or put ourselves in, the *protector* will always take our side and will do whatever it feels is in our best interests. The *protector* is our loyalist friend and is often prompted into action by triggers that link our experience of the present to past experiences. It can do this by trying to eradicate the perceived threat or by avoiding it. Whichever of these strategies it uses, our ability to protect ourselves determines to a large extent our self esteem. When our self esteem is high we tend to feel relatively safe. When it is low, we feel unsafe. When we are aware of our defensive strategies, our rational, responsible, compassionate self can control them. When we are unaware of them, it is the *protector* that tends to take control.

But what exactly does our *protector* protect us from? Apart, that is, from the obvious physical threats which the body seems to be able to deal with pretty effectively on its own? Even the *emotional self* cannot die while the body is still alive. However, hearts can be broken, egos belittled and pride wounded. We can experience sadness, humiliation, rejection, loss and abandonment. The *protector* attempts to protect us from all these feelings, and often does so by avoiding or eliminating what it believes will trigger them. Some *protectors* are so efficient that they stop us feeling altogether, thwarting the very essence of life. All *protectors* can get it wrong. For example, Sam's *protector* was wrong in responding as if all interviewers were out to humiliate potential employees, and that all relationships are doomed to end in betrayal and separation. *Protectors* can also be extremely stubborn. Its instincts and intuition may be highly developed, but its capacity for conscious analysis is fairly limited, if not absent altogether. Often, the *protector* sniffs out danger when there isn't any, just as a dog barks at a harmless post man or as a horse shies at a traffic cone.

When we feel anxious or panicky it is often because the *protector* has identified some combination of smells, images, textures, sound and tastes that signal danger. This assessment is often based on past experience. For example, Sam's group interview scenario contained similar elements to that of the classroom scenario in which he experienced acute humiliation at not being able to recite the seven times table: Both included a person in the role of judge, a group of people watching on and potentially difficult questions. Likewise, Sam's experience of his parent's separation in which his mother betrayed and abandoned his father for a man Sam had never met and for reasons Sam may never know, would likely prompt Sam's *protector* to push the panic button were his partner to tell him she was going on a work seminar with a male colleague Sam did not know.

No matter how much Sam's *rational self* insists the interviewer is not a tyrant trying to humiliate Sam, or that his loving partner is simply complying with her work duties, the *protector* will continue to *protect* Sam by either avoiding the danger, or until Sam's more rational *parent self* takes control of proceedings.

If the *protector* is left to its own devices, it may act regardless of whether the threat is real or not. These potentially inappropriate and self-defeating responses may serve to limit any potential pain, but they also thwart any potential gain. In other words, with the *protector* in control, Sam is unlikely to get the job he wants, or the intimacy and trust he yearns for.

Whatever protective strategy the *protector* uses, whether innate or acquired, aggressive or defensive, all require an enormous amount of skill and experience to be effective. These resources and skills can include intuition, intelligence, cunning, the ability to argue convincingly, brute force, stamina and a fertile imagination. Re-training the *protector*, then, can be one of the most rewarding parts of overcoming anxiety and panic, as once a person is less in need of protecting him or herself, the same skills and resources can be dedicated to opening up an exciting new world of potential and possibility.

A fascinating example of this is that of a client of mine who, for reasons of his own, had managed to accumulate two parallel lives, each with a house, wife and children. To protect himself from the fallout a potential collision of these two worlds would generate required an inordinate amount of forward thinking and planning, bucket loads of inventiveness for new and feasible excuses to "get away", and some pretty impressive self-denial. He managed to keep his two "lives" separate from one another for nine whole years! Disregarding for one moment the ethics, or lack of them, associated with such an enormous lie, the skill, aptitude and resourcefulness necessary to sustain it never ceases to amaze me. It was the equivalent of juggling a hundred balls behind the back. Inevitably, of course, he dropped one. Hence his visit to me. Although he was naturally extremely distraught, as were both his families, the skills he had honed and improved over the years to avoid such an outcome were mind boggling and, when put to better use, would propel him into the world of business as an extremely successful negotiator. Unfortunately, however, for a long time he found himself compelled to lie even when he had no need.

Sam also developed exceptional abilities in his attempt to protect himself from being judged and abandoned. And, just as the man with two lives often found himself compelled to lie, Sam's defensive strategies became engrained into his personality. In other words, Sam protective strategies and his personality were somehow intertwined. He reacted habitually to threats and was prompted, not by his desire to grow and evolve, but by his *protector's* desire to protect him from potential pain. Sam, instead of responding in the way he would have liked, responded how he had become accustomed to in order to survive. In other words, his accumulated fear of humiliation and abandonment outweighed his desire to succeed and to trust. The client with the double life may have liked to have channelled all his energy, love and creativity into one family but his *protector* engineered a situation in which he got all his needs met without the risk conflict arising between them.

The *protector as* guardian of our identity

The *protector* is also guardian of our identity. More specifically, it defends our ideas, beliefs and convictions that form part of who we are. For example, one of Sam's beliefs about himself is that he is an honest person who maintains that lying is wrong and counterproductive. Though Sam is by no means a saint, and will sometimes lie to "protect" himself, his belief that he is fundamentally an honest person is something he values. If this belief is attacked or threatened he will defend it ardently because, were his belief to be undermined, his very sense of self would be threatened. Indeed, there are those that feel so insecure about their identity that instead of limiting themselves to defending their beliefs, they try to impose them on others. On an individual scale, this often results in squabbles, arguments, separation and divorce. On a grand scale, it often results in war.

Protective strategies

Most of us have a whole array of protective strategies at our disposal. Sam is no different. The following extract from his *journal* contains many of the most common ones, some of which you may recognize. The account relates to the series of defensive postures, attacks and counter-attacks made in response to a phone call Sam answered that was made to his partner, Liz.

Sam's journal: The phantom phone caller

When Liz's phone rang, she was busy in the study. *You take it,* she called out. So I did. The caller hung up.

Liz said *they* had probably been cut off.

People don't get cut off anymore, I answered, and added silently to myself, *they have affairs.*

Looking back on it now I linked the call, consciously or otherwise, to one that had been made several years earlier to a previous partner of mine. On that occasion the "phantom" caller transpired to be my partner's lover, and I was left feeling betrayed, angry and ultimately single.

This time, in order to avoid a similar outcome, I defended myself by building a wall around myself. This wall took the form of a stubborn silence, and its purpose was not just to protect me but also to punish my partner by subtly ignoring and rejecting her. Although building a *wall* may appear to be a rather rudimentary protective strategy, the act of isolating someone for any lengthy period of time requires resilience, consistency and the ability to pretend that your curt, bristly responses and non-committal answers are completely normal. This silent siege was in part due to an internal conflict I struggled to resolve. On the on hand, a self-aware and rational part of me believed that I was both overreacting to and distorting quite horribly a quite straightforward occurrence, and that to accuse Liz of betrayal would needlessly damage our relationship, perhaps irrevocably. On the other hand, a mistrusting and wounded part was convinced that Liz was betraying me.

My mistrusting, wounded part hoped that Liz would eventually confess. My self-aware, rational part rather hoped that my anger and jealousy would eventually subside. Neither occurred. Not because of anything I did, but because Liz was no fool and because, even if my anger and fear were to subside, all the accumulated, repressed anger and jealousy would simply simmer away under the surface, only to surge up with even greater force the next time a "phantom caller" appeared and disappeared. So I did not persist with the wall. Had I done so, my mistrusting *self's* fears, fuelled by my imagination, would have grown to such an extent that I would have felt impelled to take flight and abandon the relationship, probably dumping, on my way out, all my anger, fear, shame and pain onto my innocent partner. Alternatively, I would have put Liz under such intolerable pressure that she may have felt forced to leave, thus confirming my world view that all relationships end in betrayal and abandonment. Either way, our relationship would have suffered an unnecessary and perhaps fatal blow.

Fortunately, neither of the above occurred as Liz, cottoned on pretty quickly to the fact that something was wrong and asked me directly what the problem was. During the ensuing conversation, the fears of my mistrusting *self* overwhelmed the self-aware, rational *self* and I began to accuse the phantom caller, whom I was now sure was a *he*, of having dishonourable intentions, reasoning, or rather assuming, that had *he* been just a friend he would not have put the phone down. Liz defended the caller by suggesting that, even if *he or she* had not been cut off, *he or she* may have felt embarrassed or thought that *he or she* had called the wrong number. This fuelled my mistrusting *self's* suspicions even further, not because of the unlikelihood of getting the wrong number, but because I was on a roll and, raising my voice, I began to accuse Liz of colluding with her friend, reeling out, as evidence a whole list of previous examples of dubious "dead" phone lines, wrong numbers and drained batteries. In effect, I was trying to bully Liz into confessing by aggressively attacking her with unsubstantiated evidence of similar acts of betrayal dredged from a distant past. My rational, self-aware *self* may have been somewhere in the background advising me not to, but by this time it didn't stand a chance.

The act of aggressively attacking someone with accusations of past misdemeanours, no matter how unsubstantiated or unconnected, requires a fair amount of skill. Firstly, it needs a considerable amount of energy and conviction to sustain it. Secondly, to unearth events from the distant past and to distort them in such a way that they can be used as evidence requires the memory of an elephant, the artistry of a magician and the ethics of a salesman.

However, no matter how skilful I was at proving a point, I could never see past my own pain and connect with the more the rational, compassionate, self-aware *self* which, at least, would have been able to negotiate me out of what was now a lamentable

> situation. Alternatively it could have surrendered my position by artfully backtracking, by apologising or by simply pleading guilty. Or were I to feel brave enough to acknowledge my fears and insecurities I could hope that Liz would be compassionate enough to forgive my lamentable behaviour. Alternatively, though less likely, my fears would overwhelm me and I would involuntarily display my vulnerability and fear. Unfortunately, none of the above transpired. I stomped out of the room and we never spoke about it again. Or rather, until the next "phantom" called.

In the above episode, Sam's behaviour was fuelled by the experience of a past betrayal, and his emotions associated with it were so intense that he could not see past his own pain. Regardless of whether the "phantom caller" was his partner's lover, Sam used the three most common protective strategies to ensure that he avoided painful feelings and to exact revenge. These are *defence* (the wall), *attack* (accusations) and *retreat* (stomping out of the room).

The *protector* as personality

Like Sam, we all have at our disposal these protective strategies. Naturally, each individual tends towards the use of one rather than another. A shy person, for example, may be more prone to the use of defensive minded strategies, whereas an outgoing person may tend towards more attacking ones. It could be argued that the protective strategies we use are, in part, determined by our *personalities*, or that our *personalities* are partly defined by the way we protect ourselves. Shy, aggressive, provocative and slippery are all ways to describe *personalities* and all of them are protective strategies.

Sam had his own unique personality and, although in the incident of the *phantom phone caller* Sam used a variety of protective strategies, there was one strategy that Sam used much more often, and that was inextricably linked to his *personality*. This strategy developed over time, both as a consequence of the role models he grew up with, especially his parents, and of the skills he acquired along the way.

Like most of us, Sam's recollection of his past is vague. It may be that every feeling, smell, sound, texture, taste and sight is embedded somewhere in Sam's unconscious mind and can be triggered at any time, but the act of piecing together someone's entire history is another matter. Even those memories that appear crystal clear to someone can change over time and cannot be verified. Certainly, Sam's awareness of those attributes he shares with his parents is, at best, distorted and biased. The following account of how Sam's *dominant defensive strategy* developed is then, how it could have happened, rather than how it definitely happened. The account was written by Sam in conjunction with myself.

Sam's lethal weapon

When I was a baby I didn't think about how to protect myself because I couldn't think. When I felt unsafe, for example, when I was separated from my mother, I would cry. My mother would return, and I would feel safe again.

As I developed physically, emotionally, intellectually and socially, I learned and experimented with other ways of ensuring I felt safe. These were initially rudimentary ways, like specifying what I wanted by naming it, such as *Mummy* and *no*. When I began to venture off on my own to explore the garden or the next shopping isle in the supermarket, I discovered that simply shouting the word *Mummy* did not always have the desired effect. Mummy, I was beginning to realise, was a separate person with a life of her own.

To partially cater for the loss of what, until then, I had experienced as constant and unconditional protection, I developed a parallel relationship with something that would not only always be immediately available, but that would also never judge me or have any of its own needs - a teddy bear. And when my teddy became inappropriate, I substituted it for the more adaptable and versatile *imaginary friend*. This *imaginary friend* was born around the same time that I became particularly obsessive-compulsive in my behaviour. I would, for example, always look under my chair before sitting down, I felt compelled to touch things a certain number of times, and I never went through a door without someone else passing through it first. This obsessive-compulsive behaviour was more prominent when I felt out of control or unsafe and acted, I suppose, as a mechanism that allowed me to believe I controlled what happened to me – a kind of offering to appease the "higher powers".

As I got older, I developed the ability to observe the reality underlying some of the stories my parents had told me to entertain me and possibly to instruct me in the ways of the world. For example, I discovered that Father Christmas was actually daddy. As realities like this began to seep in, it became increasingly difficult for me to maintain my relationship with my *imaginary friend*. My need to feel safe, however, increased rather than diminished as it was at this time that I was jettisoned, all alone, into the big wide world. I was to begin school. On my first day, I stood in the middle of the tarmac playground, armed only with a bag of marbles in one pocket and a pack of Trump cards in the other. I rolled the marbles around in my fingers. With my other hand I flicked through my aeroplane Trump cards. I knew the cards back to front. I knew, for example, that the Harrier Jump Jet was the fastest, most powerful, the most manoeuvrable, and the most sought after.

Hands in pockets, clutching my possessions, I scanned the playground. The other children were all dressed in the same school uniform. They seemed bigger than me and huddled in pairs or small groups, avidly exchanging stories, comparing marbles and pony tails. Only a few children were alone, like I was. They stood in corners or skirted the playground perimeter. One boy was furtively looking in my direction. Slowly, we made our way towards one another, both drawing marbles and Trump cards from our pockets at the same time. His name was Roderick Pike and he became my first "bestest" friend. Unlike my *imaginary friend*, this *real friend* had a life of his own that did not always include me. When we were together, I felt fine. When we were apart I felt vulnerable and alone. I needed more friends. The more the better because school, my new home from home, had a lot more people in it than my family. I was not getting the attention I was used to and craved. I certainly didn't feel special or loved, or that I belonged. And I wanted to feel them. I wanted to be popular and to achieve this I needed to become the most colourful, shiniest, biggest marble and have the speed and dexterity of the Harrier jump jet. I needed skills and a personality.

My main skill was to run fast, and I was a good dribbler of a football. I dedicated my time honing these skills and affiliated myself to the team that had just won the FA cup. It worked. At playtime, everyone wanted me in their team. I belonged.

Being popular, in the playground at least, significantly increased the size of my ego. I was a cocky little brat. However, at such a young age my ego, although big, was extremely fragile and it was at this time that the security afforded me by my family crumbled around me when my parents separated. It was also at this time that I experienced the humiliation of not being able to recite the seven times table in front of my class, and the shame of wetting myself and having to wear the number seven badge. I was too old, or too young, to run away. I felt powerless and alone. The teacher, and even my parents, may not have been aware of how I felt. Indeed, the teacher may have genuinely believed that by making me wear a badge with seven on it he was motivating me to study harder, and that it was therefore in my best interests. Likewise, my parents may have deemed that a separation would be less traumatic in the long term. The outcome of both events, however, was that my confidence and self-esteem were severely knocked.

Fortunately, I was able to bolster my self-esteem on the football pitch and, I was beginning to discover, through the hearts of girls. Scoring goals and "scoring with girls" made me feel special and secure again. Unfortunately, though, losing and being dumped made me feel even more vulnerable and unsafe than before. To minimise this potential loss and pain, I learned to choose my adversaries wisely and, with regards to relationships, to get my disappointment in first. In other words, I would play people I could beat and break up with girls before they broke up with me. Or simply had more than one girlfriend at a time, just in case.

These strategies did not really bolster my self-esteem or reduce my mistrust of women. Any potentially humiliating defeat or meaningful romantic attachment remained, on the one hand, something that I avoided at all costs, and on the other hand, something I found myself embroiled in over and over again, in an attempt, perhaps, to change the outcome.

The only thing I was sure about was that I wanted to avoid the shame I associated with being abandoned and humiliated, and my self-protective instinct drew on every strategy available to me, innate or acquired, to ensure that I would not have to experience them again. Perhaps the most obvious of these strategies would have been to avoid any situations that might lead to them, but as I grew into a young adult, potentially painful situations and people that could potentially cause me pain presented themselves that were increasingly difficult to avoid, such as job interviews, meetings, private functions and workshops full of interesting and attractive people. All were situations in which I could potentially be humiliated, or people that could potentially betray me. I needed an alternative, more sophisticated way of protecting myself. The one that came most naturally, and which I was most gifted at, certainly on the football pitch, was that of turning defence into attack. It worked like this. When I met someone I feared possessed the potential to humiliate me or to uncover my vulnerable core, I would put them on the spot by bombarding them with a series of questions aimed at uncovering their own vulnerable core. I became, ironically perhaps, the potential humiliator - the teacher. Instead of eliciting times tables, I elicited hidden thoughts and feelings. Some people found my propensity for bypassing the often frivolous nature of "chit chat" and cutting straight to the core somewhat refreshing and liberating. Others found it insensitive, rude, invasive and slightly obnoxious.

Whether this direct and possibly invasive personality was liked or disliked, as a protective strategy it required some skill, the main one being to elicit intimate information in a spontaneous, non-threatening and disarmingly child-like way. The following episode includes an example of how this personality behaved.

I had been invited by a friend to a party to which an academic I much admired was going. Only hours before the party was due to begin my friend called me to say that he was unable to accompany me. I didn't dare go on my own, but however hard I tried to wriggle out of the engagement, my friend somehow cajoled me into going, and I soon found myself walking into a hotel function room full of strangers. Instinctively, I searched out a familiar face. The only person I recognized was the imposing academic. I myself did not have a formal education and, although I would never have admitted to it, I found the presence of credited and recognized intellectuals intimidating.

Just like on my first day at school, I was alone amid a group of people whom I felt were "bigger" and more important than me, and all of whom seemed to know each other. And just like on my first day at school, I searched for something familiar to hold on to. Instead of marbles and Trump cards, I armed myself with a drink

> and nibbles and began milling in search of a conversation to weed myself into. Eventually, I overheard two women discussing the merits of an abstract painting hanging on the wall. The work of art was composed of what appeared to be splattered paint.
> "My nephew did that one on his sixth birthday," I interrupted.
> The two women looked at me, blankly. So I continued.
> "I remember because he ruined a little girl's dress in the process and she had to change into a pair of my nephews pyjamas."
> "Really?" said one of the women, unsure perhaps as to whether or not to take me seriously.
> "Thomas the tank engine, I think they were. The pyjamas, I mean. That's why I remember. I had a pair just like them. Didn't we all! God knows how the painting got to be here. What do you think of it?"
> Given that the two women were guests at a private function and had never met me before, it would have been difficult for them to have challenged me openly. And the painting could, actually, have been authored by a six year old. For them to believe me, on the other hand, would have made their previous comments about the merits of the painting slightly embarrassing. I had, in one deft swoop, cut through the socially and intellectually acceptable veneer and exposed an uncertain core. And it wasn't mine.

When I met Sam for the first time, this candid, provocative and outwardly confident personality was the one that he presented to me. It was his *social personality for new people* and his principle protective strategy. Sam had many other ways of protecting himself in the presence of others, but the one he used most often and which people often seemed to associate with Sam was this irreverent and disarmingly child-like provocateur. Sam gave his *protector* following characteristics.

Sam's Protector

Name: Cocky Sam

Character: Cheeky, curious, rebellious, direct, spontaneous, irreverent

Needs: To be in control

Resources: Observant, intuitive, instinctive, quick thinking, witty, inventive, imaginative

There are obvious short term advantages to having a competent and skilful *protector*, but there are disadvantages in the long term. For example, in the episode of Sam and the abstract painting, Sam's strategy may have given the two women no time to ask any potentially humiliating questions of their own, but it would have been difficult for Sam to form any kind of "real" relationship with them based on mutual understanding and support. Also, Sam would be unable to maintain his protective strategy for any substantial period of time. Sooner or later, other aspects of his character would become evident as his capacity to "entertain" waned. Sam may have succeeded in appearing confident and intimate, but this deceptive exterior was simply deflecting attention away from his own vulnerable core.

It is worth noting here that Sam did have other ways of behaving that were extremely engaging, warm, intimate, honest and respectful. It was only when plunged into the company of strangers that Sam's fear of being "found out" prompted him to disguise his softer, inner core. So well did he hide it, and so skilled was he at protecting it that few people got to glimpse it. Even Sam himself, at times, lost touch with it. Many of my most academically and professionally successful clients who felt unworthy and lacked self-esteem shared Sam's fear of being "found out" to be "a fraud".

Popular *protector*s

Most of us, especially those who suffer from anxiety and panic, have a variety of protective strategies we are skilled at. However, we tend to have one that we use more often than others and that reflects, or defines, our social personality. The following list of protective strategies includes some of the more popular ones. I have divided the strategies into three loosely defined categories: *Attackers, Defenders* and *Peace offerers.* The following definitions are only for the purpose of recognition, and as such, I have limited their descriptions to casual, even tongue in cheek, stereotypes. I have not created a category specifically to include the idea of retreating or 'running away' as a defensive strategy as all of them are, in essence, forms of avoidance.

Protective strategies **The Attackers**

Name	*Strategy*
The Questioner	By continuously bombarding someone with questions, we keep the focus away from ourselves. The equivalent of being the one with the spot light.
The Nasty Guy	By hinting at our ability to cause pain, others become wary of us and tend to remain at a safe distance. The wild animal of *protectors*.
The Loud Talker	By talking loudly we imply that we are confident and dominant. The equivalent of a frog puffing up its skin.
The Close Talker	By invading someone else's personal space, people naturally tend to back off. The equivalent of having bad breath.
The Seducer	Being desirable endows us with the power to reject or accept the enamoured. The closest we get to being all powerful.

"Defenders" and "Peace offerers" overleaf.

Protective strategies **The Defenders**

Name	*Strategy*
The Hider	All Protectors are hiders in one way or another, whether it be behind someone or something, within a fantasy or in the past. Here, the *hider* is someone who literally never exposes themselves to unfamiliar situations, faces or places. The equivalent of being invisible.
The Know-all	As know-alls we draw the potential "adversary" into our own domain of expertise, and thus rarely likely to be outsmarted, humbled or humiliated. The equivalent of being a university lecturer.
Clever Clogs	By being clever we can often outsmart the most intelligent and aggressive potential adversaries. Like a chess player we can trap our opponent in a maze of words and ideas, regardless of whether we are right or wrong. The ultimate salesperson.
Mr & Mrs Average	By having no strong opinions, convictions or beliefs, we pose no threat and are therefore unlikely to be attacked. The equivalent of sitting on the fence.
Important Person	Important people are those of us who adopt as our own the power and prestige afforded to us by the external world, for example, by our job position, spending power or ranking. The equivalent of never leaving work.
The Logician	Using logic as the basis of our relationship with the world allows us to understand everything in black and white, and in doing so keeps us safe within a framework we can predict and control. Rather like painting by numbers.
The Controller	Controllers manoeuvre ourselves into positions where we can organize, plan, design, direct and ultimately control other people. The puppeteer of *protectors*.
Arrogant & Aloof	By maintaining an attitude of indifference we convey to others the message that if we are not connected to what is happening we cannot therefore be affected by it. A kind of self-delusion.

Protective strategies **The Defenders**

Name	*Strategy*
The Wall	Like the *Hider*, all *Protectors* use some kind of wall or other. The *Wall*, in this case, refers to those of us who literally deflect other people's attempts to connect. The *Wall* can be silent and stubborn like a rampart, slippery like an icy slope or tall and proud like a tower.
The Socialite	A polite veneer of genial sociability acts as a polished surface which deflects intimacy. Rather like a tea party.
The Juggler	The *Jugglers* among us keep different aspects of our lives separate from each other, enabling the needs of different *selves* to act completely autonomously in a way that avoids any internal conflict. The equivalent of juggling balls.
The Enigma	When we hide many aspects of ourselves, we become dark and mysterious, and people tend to either fear the worst or desire the best. Rather like being a secret.
The Slightly Mad	Being unpredictable and appearing irrational makes it very difficult for anyone to control us. People tend to keep a safe distance, just in case! The equivalent of being a firework that may or may not have gone off.
The Neutral	By never taking sides, it is unlikely that someone will feel the need to attack. The Switzerland of the *protectors.*
The Scapegoater	By deflecting potential threats onto more vulnerable individuals, we escape being threatened ourselves. The equivalent of pointing the finger.
The Groupie	By affiliating ourselves to a group that believes in a particular person or idea, we effectively multiply ourselves. The equivalent of being many people at the same time.
Joker	Making people laugh not only disarms potential threats, but often victimises someone else, including the person that threatens. A clever clown.

Protective strategies **The Peace offerers**

Name	*Strategy*
The Load Bearer	By carrying other people's "burdens", we become useful or even indispensable, and thus unlikely to be harmed. The equivalent of being an extra hand.
The Giver	Those of us who are *Givers* put the attention firmly onto the receiver. The equivalent of being a Christmas present.
The Adorer	Most people would rather be adored than abhorred. The equivalent of being a bunch of roses.

The role of mediator

Within the *Safe Space* model there is a *parent self*, a *child self* and a *protector*, each with his or her own needs, desires, fears, skills, resources and roles. But if we are to use this conceptual system to understand and manage our internal worlds, who is responsible for mediating between them and ensuring that no one *self* dominates the proceedings?

One person, of course, could be the practitioner. Alternatively, if you are using the book as a self-help manual, you can empower yourself to do the job. This role is referred to in the *Safe Space* model as the role of *mediator*.

The *mediator* is not a director, leader, or manager in the sense that it is responsible for the outcome. It does not assign roles or tasks. The *mediator* does not enforce rules other than those agreed to by those *selves* it mediates between, nor does it have the power to make decisions for any of the selves. The *mediator* effectively represents the *internal family of selves* as a whole in the same way that a family therapist provides the whole family with an environment in which each of the family's members can explore and resolves their differences, heal old wounds, determine goals and put into place new patterns of behaviour that will enable them to achieve their goals.

To effectively mediate between an *internal family of selves*, you don't have to have worked as a therapist. If you have acted as a go-between for two arguing friends, you will already have taken on the role of *mediator*. It is the role of overseeing and monitoring exchanges, ensuring that all parties involved can express their needs, and of checking that all are satisfied with the outcome.

A *mediator*, then, needs to be fair but firm, objective, consistent, impartial, non-directive, non-judgemental and able to remain focused on the bigger picture.

As with all the terms defined in *Safe Space* model, the term *mediator* is simply for reference purposes. Some people prefer to use the term co-ordinator, overseer, supervisor or producer.

For those using this book as a self help manual, it is worth remembering that the goal of all therapists, regardless of their particular school of thought, is to enable the client to function without the therapist. In other words for the therapist to become redundant. The step-by-step procedure will prompt you to develop your own *mediator*.

Summary

The *Safe Space* model distinguishes between a *physical self* and an *emotional self*. The *physical self*, our body, is singular and finite in that it can only have one set of characteristics at a time. The *emotional self* is multiple in nature and can be understood as series of layers, where each layer represents a different age and set of needs, desires, fears, resources and experiences. There can be as many layers as experiences, though, for the sake of simplicity, we can lump them together into two parts: The inner layers, or *core*, which represent the *emotional child self*, and the outer layers which represent the *rational parent self*.

The *Safe Space* model also identifies a *protector self* whose principle function is to protect us from painful feelings associated with loss, abandonment and humiliation. The *protector* responds instinctively and habitually, and sometimes does so in ways that we do not control. This is because the *protector* often bases its decision to act by connecting the prevailing circumstances to similar past circumstances which may have resulted in painful feelings. When this occurs, the *protector*, in order to protect the vulnerable *core* or *child self*, often overrides the authority of the rational *parent self*, rather like a dog disobeying the commands of its owner.

To mediate between the above *selves*, the *Safe Space* model entertains the idea of practitioner as *mediator*.

Whether or not our *emotional self* does actually have distinct layers or ages, and whether or not we have different *selves* that can act semi-autonomously, does not matter. It is merely a conceptual system that allows us to understand, navigate and manage ourselves more effectively.

The procedure outlined in the *Safe Space* model is based on the simple belief that for a child to feel safe it requires a sufficiently competent parent which if absent will prompt instinctive and intuitive protective mechanisms to "take over". Of the many protective strategies we have at our disposal, if they override the desires of the rational *parent self*, they can force us to behave in ways that are not always in our best interests. Whether protective strategies are innate or learned, individuals tend to be drawn more towards one than another.

The Safe Space procedure provides a method for achieving an internal family of selves in which a rational *parent self* takes responsibility for looking after the more vulnerable, emotional *child self* in such a way that the *protector* can employ its many skills in other more constructive and creative ways.

One of the steps towards achieving this goal is to define our own unique *internal family of selves. Step 3* of the *Safe Space* procedure is dedicated to help you achieve this. Before embarking on the procedure, the next chapter provides some tools and skills that will help you carry out some of the *tasks* set in the procedure.

3
Tools for Change

Introduction to visualizations and trance - Self-hypnosis - Hypnosis

The theory and techniques outlined in this chapter are for the express purpose of enabling you to carry out the visualization tasks outlined in the Safe Space procedure. The information is not designed as a "crash course" in hypnotherapy and should not be viewed or used as such.

Self-help and self-hypnosis

For those using this book as a self-help manual, this chapter includes a step by step procedure that will enable you to induce your own light trance-like state necessary for the *visualization tasks* in the procedure.

Psychotherapists and counsellors

For practitioners with no or little experience in hypnosis there is some additional theory and some basic hypnotic strategies and techniques that will enable you to personalise and create your own trance inductions. There is also a section on how to communicate with clients who find it difficult to do so verbally, as well as advice on how to avoid false memory syndrome. This chapter also includes a technique for managing potentially overwhelming emotions that may emerge during trance.

The techniques and procedure for the regression used in the visualization task *Parenting the child* can be found in *Step 5* of the *Procedure.*

Hypnotherapists

For recently trained hypnotherapists and those who have not practiced for a while, this chapter may serve as a refresher and, I hope, to inspire new ideas and ways of looking at the matter.

Introduction to visualizations and trance

The unconscious mind

Depending on what you believe in and what you have been trained in, you will have a particular way of perceiving and talking about the part of the mind that is not conscious. Some refer to this "part" as the unconscious or subconscious. Others call it the metaconscious. In this book, the term *unconscious* is used simply because it is a term that most of us are familiar with.

Although many aspects of the unconscious mind still remain a mystery, it is understood by most to harbour every single event, taste, smell, vision and texture we have ever experienced. It is believed to be the seat of our emotions, our imagination and our instincts, and to store all our memories, both remembered and un-remembered. It is considered to be the driving force behind all our behaviour patterns and responses, and is responsible for maintaining the body in good health. It also seems to respond to situations and events with the express purpose of avoiding pain, obtaining pleasure and ensuring survival – the so-called *pleasure principle.*

When our unconscious behaviour patterns dominate our experience, we are able to tap into the unconscious mind's ability to deal with multiple and complex instructions. It can sometimes feel as if we are on auto-pilot. However, the unconscious mind is not able to make decisions about the way it behaves. Rather, it clings to known behaviour patterns it has acquired or inherited from the pleasure principle and it acts without "thinking".

The conscious mind or "thinking" part of our mind, on the other hand, is intelligent, realistic, logical and pro-active. It may be only able to deal with a few things at the same time and is easily overloaded, but its ability to think rationally and intelligently are essential in helping us make our day to day decisions.

However, what we think or believe about things, our desires and fears, and how we respond to external situations seem to be largely dependent on the experiences and memories that are stored in the unconscious, intuitive, reactionary, dexterous "non-thinking" part of the mind. In a way then, interventions using hypnotic trance are actually a way of enable us to wake up from our day to day trance-like behaviour.

Hypnosis and self-hypnosis

Hypnosis and self-hypnosis are tools we can use to navigate around, explore and manage the unconscious mind, as well as accessing the natural resources stored within it. *Hypnotherapy* is the use of hypnosis in conjunction with other therapeutic techniques such as direct and indirect suggestion, regression therapy, uncovering techniques, parts therapy, gestalt and NLP strategies. All these techniques are employed to facilitate change by transforming self-defeating behaviour patterns and negative thoughts, and by influencing the body's autonomic functions.

All hypnosis is essentially self-hypnosis in that it is not possible to induce hypnotic trance in a person unless that person wants and allows themselves to experience trance. Self-hypnosis can be equally as effective as hypnosis and has the advantage of being immediately accessible.

Although there seems to be no "text book" definition of hypnosis - even "experts" do not seem to be able to agree on a precise definition - the average person often has very specific beliefs about what hypnosis is, many of which are associated with a variety of myths. Some of these myths are founded on mistrust of the unknown and, were they to be true, would provide ample reason for staying well clear of hypnosis and hypnotherapy. Fortunately, experience contradicts these myths. The following information aims to readdress some of the misconceptions that have arisen because of them.

Myths and facts about hypnotic trance

If you are not psychotic, do not have a thought disorder or a particularly low IQ, you can experience hypnotic trance to some degree. But only if you want to. There is nothing spooky about hypnotic trance. It is just like the ordinary, everyday trance we naturally experience when we are absorbed in a good film or a book. In other words, its when we feel we are in one place while in another. Hypnotic trance is safe and natural with no side effects. You will be aware of what is happening and of the noises around you, and you will remember what happened in your trance, just like after watching a film or reading a book. The difference between watching a film and visualizing during hypnotic trance is that, in hypnotic trance, you are the one that determines what happens and how you respond to what happens.

Hypnotic trance, rather than reducing your self-awareness and ability to act, increases them. If, on the other hand, you relax so much that you fall asleep, you will wake up naturally as you always do, safe in the knowledge that while asleep, no-one can influence you in any way.

If someone else is helping to guide you into hypnotic trance, they will have no control whatsoever over what you say or do, and if you wish to stop the process you can do so immediately by simply opening your eyes. You cannot *not* wake up from trance. You will not give away secrets, unless you want to. You can even lie if you wish, and will only comply with suggestions, including auto-suggestions, if they fit into your moral value system. In other words, you are responsible for everything you do and say.

If you are concerned as to whether or not hypnosis is anti-Christian in some way, the Catholic Church takes the view that "hypnotism is licit if used for licit purposes"[5] Hypnosis is not a magical power, nor an exact science. It is a series of established psychological techniques and language patterns which are used in conjunction with other techniques and strategies. It cannot help cure everything, but it can help overcome anxiety and panic and is perhaps one of the most under-utilised resources in health care and personal development today.

Visualizations

Whether you are an experienced hypnotherapist or are unfamiliar with the term *visualization*, we all use the same word for those *visualizations* we experience while asleep. We call them dreams. We may not know much about dreams, but we do know that while we are asleep we have them, and that while we are awake we don't have them, or at least not in the same way.

One way of differentiating between dreaming while asleep and not dreaming while awake is as follows: when we dream we are not consciously aware that we are dreaming and therefore are unable to consciously determine what happens in the dream[6]. Thus, we are not responsible for our actions or the outcome of the dream. When we are awake we are aware of being awake and are consciously able to determine what we do and how we respond, and are therefore responsible for our actions.

In other words, while asleep we cannot say to ourselves, *"Oh, I am in my bed asleep and at the same time I am flying over a mountain covered in vanilla ice-cream, and as I am really hungry and because both the me that is dreaming and the me that is asleep really fancy some chocolate, I'll just turn the mountain into a huge Easter egg.* On the

---

[5] The new Catholic Encyclopaedia

[6] I acknowledge those who believe that we are able to remain conscious while asleep and dreaming, such as those who practice shamanism and lucid dream work.

other hand, when we are awake and, for example, shopping at the supermarket, we can say to ourselves, *Yes, I am in a supermarket and in front of me is a whole shelf of chocolate and vanilla ice creams to choose from and, as I prefer chocolate, I think I'll take a chocolate one.* But we cannot turn the supermarket into an Easter egg.

When described in these terms, the experience of being asleep and being awake seem completely different. However, travelling from one state to another can sometimes be like flicking a switch. One minute we are asleep, the next we are awake. During the transition period between the two states, we may feel sleepy or groggy, and those dreams that spill over into the realm of the semi-conscious tend to be forgotten no matter how hard we try to grasp hold of the memory of them. This groggy, dream-like state is also experienced while under the influence of alcohol and drugs which, unlike being asleep and dreaming, we are able to control to varying degrees what we do and say, and are therefore responsible for our actions.

A *visualization*, as defined in this book, is the act of "dreaming" while "awake" in a way that allows us to consciously control the dream. Put another way, it is the act of imagining a *scene*, remembered or imagined, and using our conscious intention to determine what happens during the *scene* and how it ends in a way that makes us responsible for it. This "scene" can be a past experience or an imagined present or future scenario. *Visualizing*, in other words, accesses both the natural resources of the unconscious and conscious mind.

The purpose of the *visualization* tasks in the *Safe Space* procedure is to readdress how we feel about our capacity to manage events and feelings, especially those that are similar to ones we have experienced as traumatic in the past. One way of understanding how *visualizations* work is to view them as if they were dreams. If, for example, you have a bad dream in which someone is chasing you, when you awake from the dream, you will likely feel unsettled by the residual fear that spills over into your waking world. If, however, while dreaming the dream, a conscious, rational, part of you were able to enter the dream and stop, catch or eliminate whoever or whatever it was that was chasing you, on awaking from the dream you would probably feel much better. In other words, by changing the outcome of the "dream" we can change our relationship to it and therefore the way we feel about and respond to similar situations. *Visualizations* do just this.

Visualizations are often more effective if they are carried out while in a trance-like state, sometimes referred to as relaxed, altered or alternative states of consciousness. This trance-like state enables us to connect with our unconscious mind in a way that allows us to experience memories, desires and fears in present time, just as we do when dreaming, while at the same time remaining aware that we are consciously manufacturing these experiences and therefore able to determine what happens and take responsibility for it. The two principle components, then, for a successful *visualization* are a trance-like state which aids our imagination to actively create a world that feels real, and conscious intention that enables us to determine what happens.

If the idea of controlling a dream seems rather fanciful, we do it naturally more often than we may think. Daydreaming and fantasising, for example, are forms of *visualizing* in that we are simply running a "scene" in our mind towards a desired or predicted outcome. Although daydreams and fantasies are carried out when we are "awake", they are often fuelled and determined by fears and desires which prompt us to play out the same scenes, often obsessively. This suggests that the scenes are being manufactured at an unconscious rather than conscious level. In other words, we are not controlling the fantasies as much as we may like to believe.

It could be said, then, that rather than simply being either asleep or awake, we seem to be able to flit between a variety of altered or alternative states of consciousness. This brings us to the notion of having different states or levels of awareness. Present day occidental psychology defines four main states of awareness, referred to as *Beta*, *Alpha*, *Delta* and *Theta.*

The *Beta state* is defined as the experience of being awake, conscious and pro-active. It is characterized by high brain waves or *Beta* waves. The *Alpha* state can loosely be defined as being awake and relaxed and thus more open to suggestion, more able to access memories and store new information. It is characterised by slower *Alpha* waves. The *Delta* state we experience while asleep when we process information through dreams. The *Theta* state is a deep sleep in which we do not dream. When we are "awake" we naturally oscillate between *Beta* and *Alpha* states and the brain emits both *Beta* and *Alpha* waves. Under hypnosis, the *Beta* waves slow down to *Alpha*, which effectively function as a door between the conscious and the unconscious mind, thus enhancing communication between the two. The *Alpha* state, then, is extremely conducive to the task of *visualizing* as we can effectively draw on both the imaginative powers of the unconscious and on our conscious will.

Levels of trance

Many people who experience trance through hypnosis or self-hypnosis find that it is different to what they expected, often remarking that they could not have been in trance because they were aware of everything around them. This conclusion is often the consequence of the preconception that while in trance we are unaware of what we do or say, and so, if we remain conscious of everything that is happening in the external world, our experience does not match our expectation and we conclude that something must be wrong. This belief that we are not aware of what is happening in the external world is perhaps one of the most common misconceptions about trance. Our awareness is actually heightened and our perceptions more finely tuned. In fact, the *visualization* tasks set out in the procedure would not be possible were we not conscious because the goal of them is to determine the outcome of the *visualization.*

This state of being conscious within the world of the unconscious can be best described by using the analogy of the land and sea in which the land is the conscious mind and the sea is the unconscious mind. In this analogy, the trance-like state or *Alpha* state would be the equivalent of paddling, wading or swimming near the shore at a depth you can put our feet down. The further away from shore, the deeper the "level" of trance. The following *levels of trance* are all ones we experience on a day to day basis and referred to in this book as *shallow trance*, *medium trance* and *deep trance.* The *level of trance* required for the *visualization tasks* in this book is shallow to medium.

Shallow trance (Lethargy)

If you have ever wondered how you managed to arrive somewhere driving your car because all the while your attention was on something else, you have been experiencing *shallow trance.* It occurs when your unconscious mind is engaged in one task, for example driving, while your conscious mind is engaged in another, for example, your plans for the weekend. It is as if you were running on auto-pilot. In *shallow trance* you are more rooted in the external world than the internal one because your conscious mind always has "an eye on the road".

Medium trance (Catalepsy)

If you have ever cried, winced or felt your heart race because of something that happens during a film, you are experiencing *medium trance.* You know that protagonists in the films are actors and actresses and that in front of them are spotlights, cameras, film crews and mobile cafes, but you respond as if the story was really happening.

If the film were being projected in a packed cinema, it may take a while for you to "get into" the film, perhaps because the person next is unwrapping a boiled sweet. Yet good films always manage to grab your attention and draw you in, so much so that when the film ends and the lights flicker back on, you are sometimes slightly surprised to find yourself in a room full of people. This state of being enthralled in a film or book is effectively a *medium trance* state.

Although when watching the film, you do not project the images yourself, the emotions you experience are directly or indirectly related to your own experience. You are, in effect, rooted more in the virtual world than in the external one, and if someone on the other side of the cinema were to get up and leave, you would probably not notice them. However, should the person next to you ask to get passed, you would easily and naturally return to the external world and get up.

In the *visualization* tasks in the *Safe Space* procedure, the only real difference between them and watching a film is that, when visualizing, you are the actors, the film crew and the director. You are effectively watching a film of yourself that you have made.

Deep trance (Somnambulism)

Deep trance is something we sometimes naturally experience while in the process of waking up. It is the experience of being rooted in a dream, yet just aware enough to be able to influence what happens in the dream. This deep state of trance is not required for the *visualization* tasks set out in this book.

The Esdaile State

The Esdaile state refers to the ultra deep state of hypnosis beyond deep trance during which surgical procedures such as amputations can be carried out. Someone in this state will hear the voice of the person inducing the trance but will be unable to carry out any of the suggestions. The Esdaile state is not required for the *visualizations* in this book.

The trance experience

How trance is experienced differs from person to person. In fact, you could say that there is no such thing as a trance state, only various altered states of consciousness characterised by a combination of the following internal changes and processes. It would be unusual for someone to experience all of them at once.

Illogical things appearing logical

When experiencing trance, as when dreaming, situations that may appear unusual and illogical in the waking state are easily accepted and explored. For example, experiencing being more than one person at the same time or the existence of animals that can speak in our own tongue.

Time travel

Trance logic, like dream logic, naturally enables you to get older or younger, to travel back to the past or forwards to the future, to metamorphose into something else, to be in two places at the same time or in the same place at two different times.

Effortlessness

While in trance, ideas, images and feelings often happen effortlessly.

Sensory changes

Ideas appear clearer, sounds appear crisper or duller, outcomes seem more definite, feelings stronger or more detached.

Fixation

Because your awareness is effectively heightened during trance, once you begin a particular train of thought or embark on an idea or journey, it is easy to become fascinated by them.

Things appear more meaningful

You experience the events and feelings as real, essential, profound and life changing. When you "come out" of trance, these same feelings and events may seem unreal and superficial.

Time distortion
When you "come out" of trance what seemed like ten minutes may have been an hour.

Memory distortion
Although you can often recall every single detail of what happened during trance, your memory can become unclear and disordered. This tends only to be the case for deeper levels of trance.

Physical changes
If you are inducing trance in someone else, a combination on the following physical changes allow you to monitor the development of the trance: facial muscles relax, often characterized by skin colour changes. Muscles twitch. Swallowing becomes more frequent and tummies rumble (peristalsis). Eyes can be seen to move rapidly behind the eyelids (rapid eye movement [REM]) indicating a shift in brain waves or that the person is visualizing. Breathing patterns change. Some people breathe faster. The majority slow down. The depth of breathing can also change from shallow to deep. When people visualize they tend to breathe from their chest. If a person keeps their eyes open, the eyes often glaze over and pupils can dilate in accordance with how receptive the person is. The rate of blinking may also change.

The above phenomena all naturally occur when we are not in trance. That which indicates that trance is developing is not the phenomena themselves, but how they develop and change. Different levels of trance prompt different changes.

Trance and drugs

Trance can also be induced through the administration of medicines and recreational drugs. However, there is a crucial difference between drug induced trance and hypnotic trance. When someone's state of consciousness is altered by drugs, the person is not in control of what happens. As the *visualization* tasks set out in *Safe Space* procedure are aimed at enabling the individual to self-determine how they behave and feel, being able to control the process is fundamental if it is to be effective.

Self-hypnosis and hypnosis

If you are using self-hypnosis to create your own trance-like state, the process will be influenced by how much you believe in the process, your level of motivation and your natural ability to enter trance, which increases with experience.

If you are using hypnosis to induce trance in someone else, your ability to gain their trust will also determine to a large extent the effectiveness of the process.

However, if I were to name one particular condition for achieving a trance-like state, it would be that of the person's readiness to *let go*. In theory, all the other determinators merely serve to increase the likelihood of *letting go*. Regardless of how good a practitioner's techniques are, if the subject resists or distrusts in the process, they will not relax. In other words, trance cannot be induced, it can be allowed to be induced.

One could argue that *letting go* is not that difficult. After all, it requires no skill or effort and can be wonderfully liberating. In fact, we cannot actually *let go*, but rather we simply stop holding on. It is one of those rare cases where the less you do, the more you achieve. The less you try, the easier it is. However, many people associate letting go with being out of control, rather like falling and having nothing to grab hold of. Although hanging on, or being in control, can sometimes be tiring and extremely hard work, the idea of falling can feel a little scary, especially if someone else is prompting us to do so. In trance, however, the idea is to be *in control of letting go*, just as you are in control of holding on.

The depth of trance you reach is determined to some extent by how deep you allow yourself to be. Thus, all hypnosis is effectively self-hypnosis.

Self-hypnosis

For the benefit of those working on their own, self-hypnosis is the act of inducing your own trance-like state. The procedure for self-hypnosis set out below follows essentially the same procedure for inducing trance in someone else using hypnosis. The fundamental differences are that self-hypnosis does not use verbal language strategies and does not require the building of rapport and trust with another person.

The *Safe Space* procedure is simple and brief enough to commit to memory. If you find that the procedure does not work for you, do not force it. Either try it on another occasion or record the *Safe Space induction script* offered in the following section.

Whichever path you choose to follow, the more you experience trance using self-hypnosis, the easier and more effective it becomes.

Safe Space **procedure overview for self-hypnosis**

The procedure includes up to six stages: *Preparation; Induction; Special place; Deepener; Task; Awakener.*

Preparation involves creating a state of mind and body that is receptive to trance. The *Induction* is the process of inducing the trance-like state. *Special place* involves creating a place of calm and safety that can be accessed at any time during the *task*. This part is optional and only usually included when the *task* is likely to prompt uncomfortable feelings. The *Deepener* deepens the trance state and can also act as a bridge to the "place" your *task* takes place. All the *tasks* in the *Safe Space* procedure use *visualizations* in order to achieve a specific goal. The *Awakener* is the process of returning to full consciousness.

Safe Space **procedure prompts**

In order to make the procedure easier to commit to memory, each stage has been divided into the following few identifiable *segments*.

Preparation:	Be comfortable - foment belief - form intention - create *special space* trigger
Induction:	Outside - eyes closed - inside - small things - different things - transforming things - in control of holding on - in control of letting go
Special place:	Prompt and explore *special place* - anchor *special place*
Deepener :	Counting down from ten to zero
Task:	*The procedure for all task are included in Chapter 4: The procedure*
Awakener:	Counting up from one to ten - eyes open

Safe Space **procedure for self-hypnosis**

Preparation

Be comfortable

Comfortable can mean lying down on the floor or sofa, sitting on or slouching in a chair. Some people use mood enhancers such as candles, incense and relaxing music. Others do not. Make sure you are warm enough as when you relax your heart rate decreases and your body's capacity to keep itself warm reduces.

Being *comfortable* also means not being disturbed, which means ensuring that your phone will not ring and that no-one will intrude through the door. You may want to put a "do not disturb" sign on the door. Noises such as phones ringing and people chatting in other rooms, or the sound of footsteps and traffic outside can, if used effectively, facilitate rather than hinder the experience of trance, as long as they are not excessive.

Foment belief (optional)

Once you are comfortable, you may wish to flex your mind's "muscles" a little. The following exercise not only allows you to do this, but also facilitates the process of relaxation, focuses the mind, enhances belief, strengthens conviction and increases expectation.

The procedure is as follows: Close your eyes and isolate an area of tension on one side of your body, for example, an arm or leg. Compare the difference in tension between the area you have isolated and the corresponding area on the other side of your body. Focus all your attention on the area with the most tension, take a deep breath, tighten your fist on the corresponding side, hold your breath for a second or two and use your intention to associate the tension in you body with the tightened fist. As you gradually exhale, relax your clenched fist at the same rate as clenching the fist of the other hand and notice how some of the tension in the area you initially isolated transfers over to the corresponding area on the other side. Do this any many times as necessary in order that the tension on both sides is the same.

Form intention

Spend a few moments focusing your mind on the task you are about to carry out. One simple way of achieving this is to repeat to yourself what it is you are going to do. For example, if you simply wish to create a special place to relax in, you might say something like, *It is my intention to allow myself to relax in a special place.* You could also think about those times in the past when you felt relaxed.

Intention is not to be confused with will power. Whereas will power focuses on a specific action, intention directs the mind towards the fulfilment of a general wish.

Create special space trigger (optional)

A *special place* is somewhere either remembered or imagined that prompts feelings of calm and tranquillity. Whether you choose a *special place* before or during your trance, you will need to decide upon an *anchor* that associates with this place and which you can use to *trigger* the feelings associated with it. For example, a deep breath coupled with the words "special place". Alternatively, you can use a simple movement of the body such as squeezing two fingers together. Whatever trigger you decide upon, the only requirement is that it can be implemented easily and quickly and that it is specific to your *special place.*

Induction

Outside

Focus your gaze on whatever is in front of you, ensuring that you remain comfortable. Imagine that your eyes are the lens of a camera and that you are taking a mental picture. The idea here is not to try to remember the scene in front of you, but to simply expose your senses to the scene. Make sure that your gaze remains fixed to the same spot. Your peripheral vision will pick up everything you need to.

Eyes closed

Decide on a number between five and ten. Whatever number you choose is the number of times necessary for your eyes to blink before the picture is taken and you can allow your eyes to close.

Inside

Allow whatever elements of the picture you took *outside* to form themselves *inside.* You are effectively visualizing the picture using your "inner eye". The aim here is not to try to force the picture to appear by trying to remember it, but simply to notice whatever images develop. Wait as long as you like for this to happen. Sooner or later an image will appear, even if it is not the one you expect. Spending some time watching this image evolve and transform can be rather like watching how three dimensional images seem to magically appear from two dimensional patterns on a piece of paper.

Small things

Notice the sounds around you. This could be the patter of rain if it is raining, the buzz of traffic outside, the sound of your breathing, the smells around you, the brightness or dullness of light through your eyelids, tingling sensations in your body, areas of tension, the rise and fall of your abdomen as you breathe, buzzing sounds in your ear, the roughness or softness of your clothes on your skin, the hardness or softness of whatever it is you are leaning or lying on, the warmth or coolness of the air on the back of your throat as you breathe in.

As you begin to notice these things, you may find that, instead of being a distraction, they allow you to go from outside to inside, outside in. Sooner or later, you will begin to notice things you would never have imagined possible.

If you feel a tingling in an arm or a leg, use this as a cue for the rest of your body to relax a little bit more.

Different things

Noticing the differences between one sensation and another is an extension on noticing small things. For example, you could notice the difference in tension between one area of your body and another, the difference in tightness of one shoe or sock compared to the other, the difference in temperature of one hand and the other.

Transforming things

Noticing how things transform from one thing to another is an extension of noticing the differences between things. Things that can transform can include images you see through your mind's eye, the rate of your breathing, the temperature around you and the tension, or lack of it, in your body.

In control of holding on

With your mind's eye, imagine yourself hanging from the branch of a tree. You can do this by imagining yourself looking up at the branch you are holding onto, or by visualizing an image of yourself hanging from the branch. If you have trouble visualizing either of these ways, imagine that the *you* that is holding onto the branch has his or her eyes closed, and simply sense what it is like. Whichever option you choose, a short distance below the branch there is the place you will eventually drop down to. A *special place* that prompts you to feel safe and relaxed. You may or may not know where this place is it just yet, but it will be there for you when you let go of the branch. Do not let go just yet, though. Take your time to notice what it feels like to hold on. Think about how it affects your muscles and your mind as gravity exerts its force upon you, pulling you down. Hold on for as long as you wish.

In control of letting go
When you are ready to stop holding on, let go. Rather than trying to make a conscious effort to let go, simply allow yourself to stop holding on. Do so on your out breath. You may also wish to silently say to yourself the words *in control of letting go*.

Special place

Prompt and explore special space
After you *let go*, drift down to your *special space*. You may wish to prompt your *special space* to materialize by saying the words; *a special place where I feel safe is making itself available to me now*. This *special place* may be somewhere you already had in mind, or that the subconscious spontaneously connects you with or generates, such as a memory or a place that exists in the imagination. Whatever your *special place* is, as your feet gently touch the ground, take your time to explore this place, paying special attention to the sights, colours, sounds, textures, smells and, if there are any, people and animals. Notice how this *special place* prompts you to feel.

If a visual image of your *special place* does not materialize, do not force it. Rather, just notice what it is like to have let go and to be floating in space. One way of enhancing this process is to imagine yourself floating on water, noticing how your body seems to tip one way or another, while at the same time remaining perfectly still.

Anchor special place (optional)
To enable you to access your *special place* at any time during your subsequent *task, anchor* it to the *trigger* you chose in the *preparation* stage. When you wish to return to this *special place*, simply fire your trigger.

Deepener

Counting down from ten to zero
Find somewhere comfortable in your *special place* to sit or lie down and count down from ten to zero, making sure that each number is silently spoken as you exhale. In conjunction with the numbers you could also silently repeat the words, *the more I relax the deeper I go*.

Note: For the *visualization Parenting the child*, instead of counting down from ten to zero a regression technique is employed in which you regress back in time to an event in the past. The procedure for the regression is outlined in the relevant step in *Chapter 4: The procedure*.

Task: Instructions for all tasks are given in the procedure.

Awakener

Counting up from one to ten
When you have completed your task and are ready to return to full consciousness, count up from zero to ten, ensuring that each number is counted on your in breath. Use your intention to bring back the "picture" you took at the beginning of the trance induction. Notice the sounds and sensations around you, the softness or hardness of the chair or floor, the lightness or darkness through your eyelids.

Eyes open
On the count of ten, take a deep breath and allow your eyes to open.

Dealing with possible stumbling blocks

Intrusive thoughts
Sometimes, thoughts about unfinished business of the day, people and events intrude upon our *visualization* and we feel impelled to follow the thoughts towards some kind of resolution. Simply telling yourself not to think these thoughts is counter-productive because the mind does not respond to negative commands. For example, if you tell yourself not to think of cornflakes, you cannot but think of them. There are, however, ways you can "detach" or "unhook" yourself from obsessive thoughts. One method is to allow the thoughts to occur and to simply observe yourself thinking about them, thus reframing your experience of them. Another way of reframing is to transform the thoughts into something else, like clouds, and notice how they themselves change and transform as they drift across the sky. Alternatively you can imagine the thoughts as being flies. The more you try to swot them, the more they will buzz about. Leave them alone and they will soon get bored and go off somewhere else.

Intrusive sounds
If you feel that external sounds are intruding, focus all your attention on the sounds alone, and suggest to yourself that the sounds, instead of being a distraction, help you to go inside.

Managing emotions

During some of the *visualizations* strong feelings may rise to the surface, especially during the *Parenting the Child visualization.* To deal with these potentially overwhelming feelings refer to the section entitled *Managing emotions* on page 93.

Hypnosis

This section is for counsellors and psychotherapists who have no or little experience using hypnotic trance, for recently qualified hypnotherapists and hypnotherapists who have not practiced for a while, and for lay people who are co-working together. For those using self-hypnosis, the section entitled *Managing emotions* will also be of value to you.

The section provides practical instructions on how to induce in another person the light to medium states of trance necessary for the visualizations set out in the procedure. It does not set out to provide the necessary skills and information in order for someone to set up practice as a hypnotherapist. It does, however, offer some basic theory, strategies and techniques that will enable you to create a "style" of hypnosis that reflects your personality and resources.

Introduction to hypnotherapy

Hypnotherapy, as defined in this book, is the use of hypnosis in conjunction with various techniques and strategies that facilitate change through release and relearning. These techniques and strategies include direct and indirect suggestion, visualizations directed by the client (open screen imagery), visualizations directed by the practitioner (programmed imagery), the use of metaphor and story telling, uncovering techniques, dialogue with the unconscious, dialogue between parts of the unconscious, regressions and progressions, counselling skills, brief therapy strategies, neuro-linguistic programming strategies and any other psychotherapeutic interventions that can be carried out prior to, during or after trance.

Within the world of hypnotherapy there are two basic approaches, often referred to as the *Clinical approach* and the *Naturalistic* or *Utilisation approach.* The essential difference between them, as the names imply, is as follows: Someone using the Clinical approach to induce trance would do so by formally instructing and directing the client. Someone using the *Naturalistic approach* would be more inclined to do so by using feedback from the client in what appears to be a normal, everyday, conversational language. Many hypnotherapists use a combination of the two approaches, often referred to as *Integrated Hypnotherapy.*

Whatever approach you are drawn towards, both aim to help the client achieve the change they desire. Different clients respond better to a particular approach, just as different practitioners are more inclined to use one more than the other. Naturally, being able to use a combination of both approaches means that there is more likelihood of responding better to the client's needs.

The procedures and scripts offered below are as close to the *Integrative approach* as possible. The very nature of scripts, however, means a significant reduction in the possibility of utilizing feedback from the client. The following theory, techniques and strategies are to help you adapt, evolve and personalise your own trance inductions.

Hypnotherapeutic principles

The following maxims serve as basic underlying principles when working with the unconscious.

Acceptance of any new habit requires the cooperation of the unconscious mind.
i.e. Habits are by definition unconscious behaviour patterns.

Whenever the conscious and the unconscious mind are in conflict, the unconscious invariably wins.
i.e. However irrational our conscious mind believes a fear to be, we still feel fear.

All our habits, mannerisms and thought patterns are the result of past unconscious "programming".
i.e. Our opinions and beliefs would be different if we were bought up by different parents, in a different place, at a different time, in a different culture, surrounded by different people.

Will power and logic affect the conscious mind but not the unconscious mind.
i.e. If you will yourself to add up the numbers two and two, you will do so. If you will yourself to stop feeling anxious, you will continue to feel anxious.

The mind does not accept negations.
i.e. If you tell yourself not to think of flies you will think of flies.

Hypnotherapeutic laws

The laws upon which trance inductions are governed are the following:

The law of concentrated attention states that if you concentrate your mind on a single idea with exclusion of all others, the idea will become your reality.

The law of reverse action states that the more you try to stop or start doing something, the harder it becomes.

The law of dominant effect states that a stronger emotion will always dominate a weaker one. In other words, if your fear of separation is greater than your desire to bond, you will be more likely to avoid a long term relationship than to commit to one.

The hypnotic formula

In some ways, the unconscious seems to behave and learn like a child in that it does so through repetition, by responding to commands given by someone in authority, by responding to things which tune in to its need for identity, and by being told stories.

A common hypnotic formula is born from the belief that for hypnosis to be successful it requires that the client's intention to make it work is backed up by belief, conviction and expectation. A procedure for fomenting these can be found in the section *Fomenting belief* in the *Safe Space induction script for hypnosis.*

Intention and the imagination

For a *visualization* to be effective it requires intention and imagination. This does not mean that the person visualizing needs to be strong willed or imaginative. Intention, as defined in this book, is simply the act of focusing the mind on a particular task or wish. Imagination is defined here as the act of allowing images to occur in the mind. Everyone can do this, just as everyone dreams, though naturally some people are more visual than others. The induction outlined in this book is designed specifically to stimulate the process of visualizing.

Matching

Matching the verbal language of a client is a simple and effective way of gaining rapport and ensuring good communication.

Whether you use a direct or indirect language, your verbal language will be better understood and more readily accepted by the client if it matches their own language type. For example, the client may be more prone to using words that are visual in nature, such as, *I can see what you mean*, *the big picture* and *from my point of view*. Alternatively they may use words that are kinaesthetic or auditory in nature, such as, *I get your drift* or, *I hear what you're saying*. These are often referred to as representational systems and also include digital, olfactory and gustatory.

Matching and influencing the speed at which the client talks can not only be an effective way of gaining rapport, but can also be used to gradually slow down or speed up a client who is particularly nervous.

Matching the body language of the client, for example, by maintaining a similar body posture, is an equally effective tool for gaining rapport.

All matching is something we all do instinctively in order to gain rapport and approval. Being aware that we are doing it simply brings it into the realm of the conscious mind.

Language patterns for trance inductions

There are two basic ways of communicating with the unconscious mind and introducing suggestions. One way is to do so directly through the use of commands and direct suggestions such as, *take a deep breath and close your eyes*. Another way is do so indirectly through the use of a number of language strategies often associated with the more permissive *Naturalistic approach*. One of the fundamental aspects of these language strategies is the combination of ambiguity and specificness, distraction and engagement, which together excite the curiosity of the unconscious mind.

The key to these language strategies is that ambiguity in any representational system causes trance. Put another way, if you confuse the mind, it will drift off. Although the following language strategies turn up in everyday language, they are effective ways of inducing trance and will enable you to modify and expand upon the basic trance induction offered in this book. The following strategies were originally developed by Milton Erickson and later modelled by the neural-linguistic programming practitioners Richard Brandler and John Grinder to create what is known as the *Milton Model*. The titles given here to the language structure are interpretations of the original titles and have been created for the benefit of the lay reader. The original titles are included in brackets.

Generalising (Nominalization)
Generalising about things allows the client to make sense of words in their own way.
e.g. *As you relax more, so your comfort grows.*

Omitting references (Unspecified reference index)
By omitting references the client fills in their own meaning.
e.g. *There have been times in your life when you have been happy.*

Disguising suggestions as questions (Tag questions)
Disguising a suggestion as a question distracts the conscious mind from objecting to and therefore resisting a statement.
e.g. *You could relax if you wanted, couldn't you?*

Matching client's experience (Pacing current experience)
Using statements that reflect and agree with what the client is experiencing builds rapport and induces trance.
e.g. *As you sit there listening to my voice here.*

Offering the illusion of choice (Simple bind)
Using a question that appears to give the client an apparent free choice between two options allows the client to "choose" an inevitable outcome.
e.g. *Would you like to relax sitting in the chair or lying down?*

Separating the conscious and the unconscious mind (Conscious-unconscious double-bind)
By splitting the conscious and the unconscious into two separate "identities" allows the unconscious mind to respond even if the conscious mind objects.
e.g. *Whatever your conscious mind thinks about the matter, your unconscious will do what it needs in order to achieve its goal.*

Yield if you do, yield if you don't (Reverse set double bind)
By giving the client alternative ways to resist means that they yield whichever option they choose.
e.g. *You can keep sitting there and not relaxing, or you can relax, but not too soon.*

Yield whatever happens (Illusion of choice and all possibilities)
Associating trance to a particular experience the client is having and restricting the range of experiences by suggesting a number of different ones, ensures that trance is triggered by at least one of them.
e.g. *The tingling in your right hand, or left hand, or perhaps your left foot, is your cue to allow yourself to relax a little bit more.*

Associating suggestion with fact (Complex equivalence)
Following a fact by a suggestion, makes the suggestion seem real.
e.g. *As your eyes close you become more comfortable.*

Questions that are commands (Conversational postulates)
Using questions in a certain way creates a desire in the client to do something about the question, rather than answer it. It is effectively a command.
e.g. *Can you remember to be kind to yourself?*

Diverting attention away from yourself (Extended quote or tangible/oblique-dissociated introduction)
By diverting the attention away from yourself and linking the suggestion to an extended series of tenuous links is less likely to be challenged by the client.
e.g. *I once watched a person who was watching someone else noticing how the ripples in the pond grew larger as the stone that caused the ripple sank deeper and deeper...*

Engaging the mind with word ambiguities (Phonological ambiguity)
By using words that sound the same but have different meanings, the client will go into trance while sorting out all the ambiguities.
e.g. *Knowing the difference between son and sun, boy and buoy, light and light.*

Engaging the mind with sentence ambiguities (Punctuation ambiguity which include: run on sentences; incomplete sentences; pauses)
By breaking rules of punctuation and expression, the mind engages itself in creating meaning out of ambiguity.
e.g. *On your arm you have a.... watch yourself go into trance; So you are...if you can change that, then perhaps....; so you are feeling.....better now?*

Using what is happening around the client (Utilisation)
Utilising what is happening around the client in the external world can turn potentially distractive events into ones that prompt the client to relax.
e.g. *You may be surprised to discover that the sound of the traffic outside, instead of being a distraction, helps you to go inside.*

Turning a word into a command (Embedded commands)
By changing or lowering your voice to mark a particular word, you are effectively embedding a command. You can also embed a command by moving your head to one side when you say the word or phrase. Even if the client has their eyes shut, they will perceive the sound coming from a different direction.
e.g. *Today is the kind of day that it's good just to* **let go** *and enjoy the atmosphere.*

Presumptions (Presupposition)
By presupposing something will happen in conjunction with a restricted number of suggestions, you are effectively giving a command.
e.g. *I wonder whether you will go into a light or medium trance today* is the same as saying *you will go into trance.*

Associating experience with fact (Truism)
Stating something that most people experience as fact suggests to the client that they will experience the same. These statements are often preceded by phrases such as *everybody; sooner or later; you already know; You've known all along how to...*
e.g. *Most people enjoy a relaxing hot bath.*

Not trying (Not knowing and not doing)
By assisting the client in not trying too hard we facilitate unconscious and autonomous responding and dissociation rather than conscious effort. This type of phrase is often used with suggestive language such as *You don't have to....You don't need to.....Without really trying, you can...*
e.g. *Just as someone doesn't have to try to float, nor do you have to try to relax.*

The opposite happens (Apposition of opposites)
By suggesting that one experience prompts another opposite experience, we are effectively suggesting they take place. This is useful to prompt a psychological state by using a physical one.
e.g. *As your breathing slows down, so your ability to allow yourself to relax increases.*

When that happens, this happens (The implied directive)

The following combination of language strategies prompts a change to take place and also serves to clarify and reinforce the change. The strategy consists of a phrase that constricts the experience to a certain time (e.g. *as soon as*), followed by a reference to an internal event (e.g. *you have accomplished your task*) , followed by the suggestion of a physical change (e.g. *you will take a deep breath*). This combination is useful for tracking progress during a task.
e.g. *As soon as you have accomplished your task you will take a deep breath.*

Metaphor

Metaphors and stories speak directly to the unconscious mind and suggest solutions in a way that invites the client to enjoy solving their own problem. The client often makes a "movie" of the metaphor or story, and the movie in turn does the healing. Metaphors and stories indirectly suggest connections between what people already understand to be true and what they need to use or accept in order to change.

Metaphor is the language of the unconscious and triggers an inner search by the listener for the stories unique significance. There is a general cultural expectancy that stories have a point, especially metaphors and parables, and so, for many people, the mere telling of a story prompts this search.

The connection between the story and the problem must be relevant but not necessarily immediately obvious. Commands can also be embedded into metaphors.

Metaphors can also used for reframing, to decrease resistance, enhance the therapeutic relationship, to model a way of communication, help the client tap into their own resources, desensitize people from fears and stimulate interest. Metaphors are less threatening than directives, provide a non-manipulative form of communication, and are one of the easiest ways to get through to the unconscious.

Although metaphors and stories are not used in the *Safe Space* procedure, for those that are familiar with them, metaphor can be incorporated into any of the interventions.

Voice and speech

When speaking to a client, you can either do so naturally as if having a conversation, or use a combination of the following techniques. All are ways of deepening and accelerating the trance process, and some can be employed to embed commands and suggestions.

Always begin an induction with a conversational speed and tone. Gradually slow down your speed and reduce the volume as you progress through your induction. You can also introduce a gentle, falling tone, speak on the client's out breath, link words, exaggerate the "S" sounds and create a rhythm. To emphasis embedded commands, use a falling tone, pause before the command or elongate the words.

For the *visualization* tasks outlined in this book, you can employ these techniques for the inductions and deepeners. However, for the *task* part of the *visualization*, I suggest a natural, conversational dialogue. Bear in mind that a person in trance does not experience time in the same way, so allow plenty of time for the client to carry out tasks and to respond to questions. What may seem like a long time to you, may seem like no time at all to the client.

Enabling a client to communicate non-verbally

Some people do not like to speak while in trance. Even those who are happy to speak during trance can at any point feel unable to do so, for example, if overwhelmed by an emotion. However, the *visualization* tasks in the *Safe Space* procedure require some kind of communication in order that the person guiding the client can respond appropriately to what is happening. One way to enable the client to communicate non-verbally is by using a simple kind of sign-language which connects a particular gesture with a specific meaning. This type of response is sometimes referred to as ideo-motor response and is effective for answering questions that can be answered with either *yes*, *no*, *don't know* or *don't want to say.* The following three gestures and corresponding meanings seem to work with most people.

Yes = moving index finger of one hand
No = moving index finger of other hand
Don't know or don't want to say = moving index fingers of both hands

This third *I don't know* or *I don't want to say* is essential for the client in that it alleys the common fear the client might have about revealing secrets they do not wish to. It also serves to prompt the practitioner to ask the question in another way.

Experience dictates that an ideo-motor response has a greater likelihood of being accurate than a verbal response because it is a spontaneous response from the unconscious mind. Verbal responses, on the other hand, are more likely to be filtered, embellished or distorted by the conscious intellect. Still, even with ideo-motor responses there is no guarantee that the truth will emerge as people can lie using ideo-motor responses while in trance just as they can lie verbally. However, in cases when the verbal answer and the ideo-motor response contradict one another, it is unlikely that the person is aware of the contradiction and thus the ideo-motor response, which comes directly from the unconscious, is invariably the accurate one.

Avoiding False Memory Syndrome

False Memory Syndrome is when a practitioner prompts or implants into the memory of the client an event which did not take place. This often occurs when the practitioner has a preconceived notion or theory about what might have happened and, in an attempt to prove the theory, asks a series of leading questions that suggest or prompt certain answers. In other words, it is the act of fitting facts to theory, rather than theory to facts. For example, if the practitioner believes that the client experienced some kind of sexual abuse, a leading question during a regression could be, *Is the person on whose knee you are sitting fondling you?*

Taking care to avoid False Memory Syndrome is especially relevant when working with regressions and with exercises that set out to uncover the cause of a particular type of behaviour. The most effective way to avoid False Memory Syndrome is to ensure that all your questions are ones that cannot be answered with a simple *yes* or *no*. For example, the above "leading" question could be translated into, *What is the person whose knee you are sitting doing, if anything?* This type of question is called an open ended question.

Naturally, practitioners do not consciously lead clients. However, ensuring that you ask open ended questions that are non-interpretative and non-judgemental lowers the risk of inadvertently doing so.

With regards to the *Safe Space* procedure, the task of avoiding False Memory Syndrome is especially relevant when carrying out the *visualization* entitled *Parenting the child*, which involves a regression.

Managing emotions

For those using self-hypnosis, substitute the words in this section that refer to the client *for words that refer to yourself.*

The aim of this section is to provide a tool to help deal with potentially overwhelming emotions that may hinder the development of the process of change during trance. It is especially relevant for the *visualization* task *Parenting the child* which involves a regression to a potentially traumatic event.

When creating change, the person the client often has to confront someone or something that they have previously feared or experienced as traumatic, and this can prompt some pretty strong emotions to surface. When working to create change there is always the potential for these strong emotions to well up in a way that threatens to overwhelm the client. These emotions may take the form or anxiety and panic, anger and rage, or sadness associated with loss.

The aim of the *visualization* task *Parenting the child* is *not* to have the client re-experience these feelings or to recreate the traumatic scenarios that prompted them. Rather, it is designed to enable the client to re-experience or "re-write" them in a way that the outcome of the scenarios is one that leaves the client feeling more in control about how they feel about what happened. In other words, that their desire to let go of pain is greater than their habit of holding onto it. That the client's ability to confront a person is greater than your fear of them. That their propensity to forgive is greater than their impulse to take revenge or to punish.

Although the *Parenting the child visualization* is prepared in a way that allows the client to access all the skills and resources necessary to create the desired change, on occasion difficult feeling may well up in the client that threaten to thwart the task.

One way to avoid the client being "overwhelmed" is by creating a *special place* that the client can immediately access in order to recuperate and calm down. It is worth remembering, however, that the release of strong repressed emotions is the essence of change and can, in itself, be an extremely powerful therapeutic process. This is especially true when the feelings are associated with coming to terms with certain "truths". It is important then, to allow these emotions an outlet whenever possible.

Not all *emotional release*, however, creates or signifies change. It is therefore necessary to be able to distinguish between the release of emotions associated with change, and the release of emotions that impede change.

Emotional release associated with change

Emotional release, sometimes referred to as *catharsis* or an *abreaction*, is prompted by a change which implies some kind of letting go or coming to terms with a loss of some kind. This loss can be the nature of a relationship we have with other people. The loss can be of a belief the client has about themselves and the world, or that other people have about them. The loss can be that of a particular way of being or behaving they have become accustomed to.

Emotional release associated with change, as defined in this book, is the release of emotion prompted by the realisation of, acceptance of or coming to terms with a certain "truth", and of owning the feelings associated with it. The importance of enabling the client to accept and own their feelings is that, once they do so, they can learn to manage them more effectively and separate them from feelings that do not belong to them. That is to say, to separate their own feelings from feelings that have been transferred onto them by other people who do not wish to or who are unable to accept them as their own. Once the client can identify those feelings that do not belong to them, they can either give them back to their rightful owner or simply rid themselves of them.

Though the experience of releasing emotion can be a distressing one for the client, it can also be a liberating one, rather like opening a sleuth gate in order to release the build up of pressure and to allow the water to naturally flow. During the *visualization* task *Parenting the child*, this kind of *emotional release* is normal and can be expected.

Emotional discharge that can impede change

Emotional discharge differs from *emotional release* in that, whereas *emotional release* is associated with feelings that the client learns to accept as their own, *emotional discharge* occurs when they do not wish to accept or own their feelings about something because they have yet to come to terms with them. This often causes the client to *repress* or block their feelings by either denying they have them or by burying them so deeply that they forget they have them. When this occurs, the client can unconsciously transfer these feelings onto other people in a way that makes the other person feel what are fundamentally the client's own feelings. Although transference can be an excellent way of discovering how someone else feels, the subject is not part of this book's remit.

Emotional discharge can take the form of anger accompanied by blame. Often this anger and blame allows the client to avoid owning and coming to terms with their own pain or loss by deflecting it away from themselves and onto someone or something else.

Although anger is a natural emotion on the road to release or forgiveness, if the client clings onto their anger, it can also be one of the greatest obstacles on the road towards change. One way of looking at anger is to treat it as an *emotional discharge* of energy. Much like sadness, it is triggered by experiences in which someone is being, or has been mistreated. In this respect, anger and sadness are two sides of the same coin. The disadvantage of projected anger, however, is that by projecting pain onto someone else, the client makes that person responsible for it, thus placing it outside their own sphere of influence.

Often, of course, anger and blame can be appropriate, natural and useful responses to situations and people who impose things that have not been agreed to.

Special place

A *special place* in this book refers to a place in the mind the client can immediately go to rest and recuperate in order to resume a *task* that had been threatened by potentially overwhelming emotions. A *special place* is somewhere associated with feelings of calm, peace and safety. It can be a memory of somewhere visited before, a place that exists in the imagination, a place where no-one else can go or a place populated by other people and animals.

When creating a *special place* it is necessary to anchor it in a way that enables the client to connect immediately with the feelings associated with it. This is done by "anchoring" the *special place* to a trigger such as a word or a movement.

Eliciting a special place

You can elicit a client's *special place* in one of several ways. You can have the client predetermine their *special place* prior to the trance induction. You can allow the client to have their unconscious mind make a *special place* available to them while in trance. You can directly or indirectly *suggest* a *special place* while the client is in trance, for example, a garden, beach or mountain scene.

The *Safe Space induction script for hypnosis* below prompts the client to create their own safe place during trance and requires no preparation.

The *Safe Space* procedure for hypnosis

The following procedure for hypnosis follows the same basic procedure as the *Safe Space* procedure for self-hypnosis: *Preparation; Induction; Special place; Deepener; Task; Awakener.* The procedure for hypnosis differs in that language structures and strategies are used to induce, accelerate and deepen the trance process.

The script uses a semi-formal integrated approach and aims to induce a light to medium state trance. It is only original in that it uses a particular combination and order of strategies and language structures.

For those practitioners unfamiliar with hypnosis, the script is divided into sections, each with an introduction and suggestions on delivery. If the client is particularly talkative or appears a little nervous, elicit as much feedback as you can during the initial stages of the induction.

Safe Space **procedure prompts**

The procedure has been divided into the following segments.

Preparation:	Ensure client is comfortable – allay fears (1st session only) – elicit agreement - foment belief (optional) – confirm purpose of trance – set up ideo-motor response (optional)
Induction:	Outside - eyes closed - inside - small things - different things - transforming things - in control of holding on - in control of letting go
Special place:	Prompt *special place* - explore *special place* – anchor *special place*
Deepener :	Counting down from ten to zero
Task:	*The procedure for all tasks are included in Chapter 4: The procedure*
Awakener:	Inside outside – eyes open

Safe Space **script for hypnosis**

The task of the following script is for the client to create and anchor their *special place.*

Preparation

Ensure client is comfortable

Comfortable can mean sitting on a chair or lying down on the floor or a sofa. The environment will be determined by your style, job environment and clientele. Some practitioners use candles, incense and relaxing music in order to create a relaxing environment. Others opt for a more formal setting. If you are a counsellor or psychotherapist, there is probably no need to change anything in your work space. Make sure, however, that the client remains warm enough as when the body relaxes the heart rate decreases, thus reducing the body's capacity to keep us warm.

For the client to feel safe it is necessary to create and maintain some basic boundaries which ideally cannot be broken. These include a time boundary that defines the time, duration and frequency of the sessions, and a physical boundary which prohibits other people or events from disturbing the session, via door or phone. Although gaining rapport and showing respect are essential elements in gaining the trust necessary for the client to feel safe, the act of consistently maintaining boundaries is hugely therapeutic in itself. Extending this consistency to include how you greet and say farewell to the client, and where each of you sits only aids in the creation of a "safe place".

External noises such as the ringing of phones and the murmur or people in other rooms, or footsteps and traffic outside are fine as long as they are not excessive. They can, in fact, be used to help facilitate trance.

Allay fears (1st session only)

Clients that have not experienced hypnotic trance before may bring with them certain misconceptions and fears about it. To allay these fears, you can use the information from the section in this chapter entitled, *Myths and facts about hypnotic trance.* Before initiating the trance process, the following may also help. *Delivery:* Normal conversational speech.

> "I know that you know that we all experience trance naturally from time to time. It's those times when you just drift off or immerse yourself in something like a good film or a good book. Trance and hypnosis mean the same thing and all hypnosis is self-hypnosis. Today I don't know if you allow yourself to go into trance sooner or later, but I do know that you will go to just the right level of trance for you. You don't have to make any effort for this to happen. Trance, like a smile, happens all by itself, spontaneously without having to make any effort whatsoever."

Elicit agreement

As all hypnosis is effectively self-hypnosis, it is essential to elicit from the client their intention to experience trance. *Delivery:* Normal conversational speech.

> "Are you ready to experience trance. *[Wait for response]* Good....I wouldn't want you to drift off just yet...that will happen all by itself."

Foment belief (optional)
The following exercise focuses the mind of the client, enhances their belief, strengthens their conviction and increases their expectation. It also prompts the client to relax.

The procedure works more effectively when the client has their eyes closed. *Delivery:* Normal conversational speech.

> "Before going into trance, I am going to show you a way to test the power of your mind, a kind of flexing on the mind's muscles. Would it be okay to do that now?
> *[Elicit permission]*
> All you have to do is scan your body and isolate an area of tension. This may be easier with your eyes closed. Once you have isolated the area of tension you can open them again, but only if you wish.
> *[Elicit specific feedback, i.e. upper leg on left side]*
> If you were to compare this area of tension, how would it compare to the same area on the other side of your body? Again, you may find this easier to do with your eyes closed.
> *[Elicit feedback, i.e. more tense, a little more tense, a lot more tense. Alternatively you could ask the client to put the tension on a scale from one to ten]*
> When I say so, not yet, focus all your attention on the side with the most tension, your right/left side, take a deep breath, tighten your fist on that side and hold your breath for a second or two. Then, not yet, as you exhale, gradually relax your clenched fist while at the same time clenching your fist on the other hand, and notice how some of the tension transfers over to the other side.
> *[Check client has understood. Repeat instructions if necessary.]*
> Ok, you can do this now by following my instructions? Focus your attention on the area of tension, take a deep breath, tighten your fist on the side with the tension, hold your breath for a couple of seconds...one...two...exhale slowly while at the same time as allowing your clenched fist to relax and your fist on the other side

to clench. Notice how some of the tension on the first side transfers across to the other side."
[Elicit feedback. Do this as many times as necessary in order that the tension on both sides is more balanced]

Confirm purpose of trance
Spend a few moments focusing the client on the task they are going to carry out. Elicit what they want to achieve and, if possible, times when they have achieved something similar in the past. When a *visualization* involves a specific *task*, this should be elicited prior to the induction procedure. *Delivery:* Normal conversational speech.

"You are here today because you wish to enjoy relaxing in a *special place*. Is that right? *[Wait for response]* Can you tell me about times when you have relaxed before or felt really at ease?" *[Prompt client to talk about whatever emerges]*

Set up ideo-motor response (optional)
"This section should only be included for clients who do not wish to communicate verbally, and for tasks which may prompt strong emotional charge. *Delivery:* Normal conversational speech.

"If at any point you do not feel you wish to communicate with me verbally, we are going to set up another form of non-verbal *communication* that will allow you to communicate the words "yes", "no" and "I don't know" by simply moving a finger of your choice. For example, if I ask you the question, *Is your name (name of person)*? you will respond with the "yes" finger. Could you please say "yes" with the finger of your choice?
[Wait for and note response]. Thank you.
Now, if I ask the question, *Is your name Donald Duck?* you will respond with the "no" finger on the other hand. Could you please say "no" with a finger of your choice on the other hand?
[Wait for and note response]. Thank you.
Now, if I ask you the question, *What is my mother's second name?* you will respond with your "I don't know" fingers, which are both your "yes" and "No" fingers together. Could you please respond with "I don't know".

[Wait for and note response]
You can also use your "I don't know" sign for "I don't want to say". Say "Yes" if you understand, and "No" if your don't understand." *[Confirm positive response]*

Induction

Outside
The following induction stimulates the visual imagination necessary for the *visualization* tasks in the *Safe Space* procedure. *Delivery:* Normal conversational speech.

"Do you remember any of the birthday parties you went to as a child? *[Elicit and discuss response]* Do you remember any of the party games you used to play? *[Prompt, if necessary, with hide and seek, treasure hunt, guessing how many marbles in a pot, memory game in which children have one minute to memorize as many objects on a tray as they can. If the client does not offer this last memory game, introduce it yourself]*

Now, we are going to play a game similar to the *memory game* in which you memorize objects on a tray, only in this game you can't lose, no matter how hard you try to lose, because you don't really have to remember anything at all. You simply take a mental picture or what you see in front of you, and after your eyes close, to see how much of the picture imprints itself on the screen inside your mind just as dreams do while asleep. All you need to do is to find something to look at and to keep your eyes fixed on that spot. Have you found a spot? *[Elicit response and ensure that client in looking somewhere in front of them in a relaxed position]* Now, imagine that your eyes are the lens of a camera and that you are taking a picture. Just like a camera, you don't need to move your eyes because your peripheral vision takes in everything it needs to. Make sure your eyes remain fixed on the same spot, without moving. Just as with taking a picture with a camera, you don't have to memorize what you are taking a picture of because you will have a picture to look at afterwards. You don't have to worry about how long to take the picture for. Your eyes will let you when you can relax by blinking five times.

OK, keep your gaze fixed on that spot. Don't let your eyes wander even for one second."

Eyes closed

"When you blink five times, the picture is taken and you can allow your eyes to close." *[Allow as long as it takes for client to close eyes]*

Inside

When the client has taken the "picture" and closed their eyes, have them describe what parts of the picture have imprinted themselves in their mind. Try to elicit what they see through their mind's eye, rather than what they remember. *Delivery:* Normal conversational speech.

"Now, gradually, in its own time, the picture that was outside will develop inside and your mind's eye, just as it sees your dreams while asleep, can see this picture emerge. What part of the picture can you see now? What colours can you see? *[Elicit response]* You don't need to remember what was in the picture, but simply tell me what your mind's eye sees emerging. It may be that you see different things to what you saw before, or maybe the same things that have changed in some way. *[Elicit]*

And whilst you can see those things that were outside inside...you can begin to notice other outside things that are outside and that filter inside...the sounds around you *[identify sounds, e.g. the buzzing in your ears, the traffic outside, the sound of birds, the rain, the tick tock of the watch yourself drift into trance]*. And you maybe surprised to discover that instead of being a distraction, reassure you that all is well...that you are safe here...that instead of being a distraction help you to go inside, from outside to inside, outside in...knowing that you could open your eyes should you wish, or not open them should....you wish to go into trance."

Small things

Have the client focus their attention on small details, allowing them plenty of time to focus on each detail. You can either describe the details yourself, for example, by saying, *notice the lightness or darkness through your eyelids.* Alternatively you can elicit the details by saying, for example, *If you were to notice the light through your eyelids, would you say it was dark or bright...moving away from you or towards you, or not moving at all?* The following example uses the first of these to techniques. *Delivery*: Normal conversational speech.

"And as you notice those things that were outside exist inside, you begin to notice the small things....the brightness or dullness of the light through your eyelids and whether the light has the sensation of moving towards you or away from you, or not at all...the rise and fall of your abdomen as you breathe in and out...the softness or hardness of the seat...the warmness or coolness of the air on the back of your throat as you breathe in...the tightness or looseness of the ring on your finger (if ring)....the watch on your wrist (if watch)...the heaviness or lightness of your earrings on each ear (if earrings)."

Different things

Focus the client's attention on the differences between sensations. As with *Small things* you can either prompt the client to silently ponder on the differences, or you can prompt the client to verbally identify them. *Delivery*: Progressively slow down speed and reduce volume.

"And as you notice the small things you begin to be aware of the differences between them....of the difference in tightness between the shoe on your right foot and the shoe on your left foot...of the difference in warmth between your left hand and your right hand...the difference in hardness between one part of the chair that is touching you and another....the difference in the volume of my voice as if comes from one direction or another *[move head from side to side as speak]*...the difficulty or ease of the experience of telling the difference between soul and sole...buoy and boy...son and sun....tick and tock and clock and watch yourself going into trance....as you just go with the flow and flow as you grow allowing yourself to let go in a different way...like singing to yourself a song you have known for so long...have you ever had a tune in your head that you just can't stop humming to yourself...wouldn't it be nice if life were a tune that seemed to be part of you...as if your self were humming to yourself...just by being here...without having to make any effort to do anything....allowing things to happen all by themselves...by just noticing the process of *going into trance*."

Transforming things

Delivery: Progressively slow down speed and reduce volume. Exaggerate the "S" sounds, create a rhythm and emphasize embedded commands (highlighted in italics) by using a falling tone, pausing before the word or elongating the word.

> "And as you notice how the small things and the different things sometimes change and transform into other things...thoughts that wander like clouds...and images that shift and change and that only your inner eye can see....as you can notice how your breathing has changed...and as you breath out...breathing out any tension or nervousness *[speak on client's and your own out breath]*...without having to make any effort whatsoever because the unconscious mind knows how to breathe, does it not? You don't have to think about it...you know that you know because your unconscious mind knows...because your body has an *inner wisdom* all of its own...so you know more than you know you know...and with every out breath you may find that you go a tenth deeper into *trance*...and your conscious mind may find it hard to notice a tenth, and may even feel tempted to make an effort to make that tenth happen...which it does not have to because...it is nice to know that for once...*less is more*...so the less you do, the more that can be done... and that by *relinquishing* the effort to make the tenth happen, it happens all by itself...and the tingling in your right hand or your left, up there or down there is a cue from your unconscious to allow the rest of your body to *relax* a little bit more...just listening to the sound of my voice or following the images with your mind's eyes....just *drifting* and *dreaming*.... curious to know perhaps...wondering how that can happen....how you can be inside and outside at the same time...here and there....in two places at the same time...and all the while allowing another part of you to just notice the process of going into *trance*....wondering about it all...we call this the hidden observer...all the while in the driver's seat...in control of letting go...each word that I speak allowing you to *relax* a little more."

In control of holding on

Delivery: Introduce more pauses. Speak on out breath and in synch with client's out breath.

"And just as you can be in control of *letting go*, so you can be in control of holding on...and you could hold on by imagining...you are holding on to the branch of a tree...maybe the branch of a big old oak or chestnut tree...only you know...after all trees are just trees and all have branches...some branches are bigger than others but they all have bark and twigs, sometimes with leaves...and you know which branch you are hanging onto....and that below this particular branch, should you choose to *let go*, but not just yet, there is a *special place* you can gently *drift down* to...a place of *calm* and *peace*....a *special place*....because everyone has a special *place*...and most people when they allow themselves to *let go* of the branch *drift down* to this *special place*....and I know that you have a special place you could *drift down* to...but not just yet because you are still holding onto that branch...safe in the knowledge that while you are here your unconscious mind can take you there...perhaps to a *special place* you have been before, or a place that exists in your imagination, that is yours alone...maybe you already know where your *special place* is, and if you do not, your unconscious mind knows and will make it available to you when you *let go*....but I wouldn't want you to *let go* just yet...but rather remain *in control* of holding on....noticing the branch and how your hands wrap themselves tightly around it...maybe you can see your hands above you....maybe you are watching yourself holding on from a distance....maybe the you that is holding on has his/her eyes closed and you can just sense what it is like to hang on...noticing how your body gets *heavier* and your hands grow paler with the effort of gripping onto the branch because...it is only natural that gravity pulls you down...it is tiring holding on, is it not?"

In control of letting go
Delivery: As above

"And just as you can be *in control* of holding on so can you be *in control* of *letting go*....the difference being that to *let go*, rather than do something, you just do nothing...you just stop holding on...and when you do that, not yet, you will drift gently down to that *special place* that is yours and yours alone...nice to know that there is a time when *less is more*, and the less you do, the more you achieve...trusting in your inner wisdom just as you trust that you will continue breathing if you were to stop thinking about breathing...and in a moment you could allow yourself to relinquish your hold on the branch and to *let go*....and to help yourself to do that...take a deep breath *[repeat command until client takes deep breath]*....and as you breathe out....be in control of letting go...*[deliver on client's out breath]*...notice how letting go can be like floating on water...seems strange that something like a body can float on something like water...but it does....just as you can seem to tip one way or another, while remaining perfectly still...as you drift towards your *special place*...no need to kick or paddle because floating happens all by itself."

Special place

Prompt and explore special place
Delivery: As above.

"I don't know how long it will take you to arrive at your *special place*...whether it will be sooner or sooner than that...perhaps...you are *already* there...as your unconscious mind makes available to you the sounds and sights of this place of calm and peace....as you find your feet gently touching the ground...and when they do perhaps you could indicate this to me my raising a finger on your right hand *[or the hand that represents "yes"]*...because only you know where you are now in this *special place* that is yours and yours and yours alone...*[wait for response]*...perhaps it is a place you have been before or that exists as real in your imagination....where you feel safe and free to experience what it is like to be free to just be....in this *special place* that is yours and yours alone…because only you know where you are now in this *special place*…and as you sink *deeper* into *relaxation*…so your *comfort grows* and your *ease of giving* to yourself can be a source of wonder….and would it be alright to just allow yourself to *be there*….to sense this place…to *enjoy* it...to take the time to explore this *special place*...to wander around or to just sit and wonder how wonderful it is to just be here noticing all that is around you…basking in the *waves of peace and tranquillity*…without having to make any effort whatsoever...just noticing the sounds...sights...smells... senses…and as you *sink deeper* into relaxation your comfort grows...without having to make any effort whatsoever."

Anchor Special place
Delivery: As above.

"And to help deepen this sense of *peace* and *safety* this *special place* provides, and to enable you to return here whenever you wish, you could take a deep breath, and as you exhale slowly, say to yourself the words...*special place*...and perhaps you could do that now. Take a deep breath, and as you exhale, say to yourself the words *special place*...and, from now on, every time you take a deep breath and say these words your *special place* will make itself available to you."

Deepener

Counting down from ten to one
Delivery: Slow down speed and volume to minimum. Use falling tone. Say numbers on out breath and synchronize with client's out breath.

"And to help enhance your experience of being in this *special place*...if in this place there is a path with steps leading down you can follow them down...and if there is no path, perhaps there is a slope or an entrance to a tunnel...or perhaps you would just like to sit or lie down and to close your inner eye for a moment counting down with me from ten to zero...each number said on your out breath and as you take a step down the path, the slope, the tunnel, or simply floating down inside...*ten...in control of letting go...nine...eight*...the *deeper you go, the more relaxed you feel...seven...six*...knowing that at any time you can come back up by counting up or go further down...*four...in control of letting go...three*...to just the right level of trance for you today...*two*...because there is no right or wrong way to relax...*one*...and all the way down to *zero."[Zero can also be the scene of the task]*

Task: *(not included in this example)*
Delivery: Normal conversational speech

Awakener

Inside outside

Delivery: Progressively increasing in speed and volume.

> "And when you are ready to return to the present, from inside to outside, whatever images and thoughts are playing themselves out now will mix themselves with the image of the picture you took when your eyes were open and that imprinted itself on the screen inside your mind *[prompt image by identifying objects in the room]* ...and as that happens, perhaps you could notice the sounds around you *[identify]*...the smells...the weight of your body in the chair as you reflect on all those things you have experienced today and that after this session the work you have started will have continued to be healing what you have already done, today, now."

Eyes open

Delivery: Normal conversational speech.

> "You may think that coming out of trance may be a struggle and that to open your eyes may be a struggle...but life doesn't have to be a struggle and you might be surprised to discover how easy and natural life can be...just as your eyes can open easily and naturally without any effort or struggle whatsoever...and if they do...then life too will unfold easily and naturally...curious to find out as to whether they will open on the second breath you take, the third or the fourth."

Feedback

In the *Safe Space* procedure, trance is used to carry out specific *tasks*, the procedures for which are included in *Chapter 3: The procedure.* Elicit as much feedback as the client wishes to give. If the client is unhappy with any aspects of the task, allow them be so, and elicit what they would have liked to have been different. Elicit those aspects of the *task* that the client felt were positive. Not all *tasks* are successful. If appropriate, gain permission to re-do the *task*.

Dealing with possible stumbling blocks

No matter how refined your techniques are or how much experience you have at your disposal, sometimes the client does not manage to connect sufficiently with the unconscious in order to carry out the *task* effectively. There are variety of reasons for this, the following of which can be addressed in the following way.

Having a nervous disposition

Nervousness in a client is often accompanied by a need to keep talking. Introducing the following language strategy may help: *Talking is good and can be useful sometimes, and you can keep talking, and you can also not talk if you wish and relax a little bit more.*

You can also match the client's speed with a view to gradually slowing it down by slowing your own down.

Fear of losing control

This is often true of clients who ask a lot of questions about what will happen during the trance. To allay their fears, explain how all hypnosis is effectively self-hypnosis, and repeatedly introduce into the conversation the words *in control of letting go*. Reassure the client that they cannot be made to do or say anything they do not wish to.

Trying too hard

This tends to be a characteristic of super-achievers and of people who suffer from low self-esteem. To counter it, introduce into the conversation the idea of *less is more*, using examples such as going to sleep, i.e. *the less you try to go to sleep, the more likely you are to do so.*

Obsessive thoughts

People who have a lot on their mind, or tend to have obsessive thoughts often try to curtail their thinking by telling themselves to not think. The *law of reverse action* suggests that this is counter-productive because the unconscious mind does not respond to negatives. In other words, if you tell yourself not to think of cornflakes, you will think of cornflakes. To disengage a client from obsessively following a train of thought, suggest that the client allows their thoughts to play themselves out, and for the client to observe themselves thinking about the thoughts, thus reframing their relationship to the thoughts. An alternative method of reframing is to have the client transform the thoughts into something else, like clouds, and to notice how the clouds themselves drift, transform and disappear. The following analogy about flies can be useful: *Thoughts are like flies. The more you try to swot them, the more manic and annoying they seem to become. If you leave them alone, however, they tend to get bored and move on. Flies are just flies after all.*

Abreactions

If the client is overwhelmed by emotions that prohibit them from carrying out a task, take the client to their *special place* by having them fire the *special place trigger*. Only continue with the task with the client's permission. Otherwise, terminate the trance. In cases when the emotions are overwhelming, the client will themselves terminate the trance.

4
Procedure

Session number, frequency, duration and location - Procedure content - Introducing the procedure
Steps 1 – 7

The Safe Space procedure consists of 7 *steps*. Each *step* includes one or more *parts*. Each *part* contains a number of *tasks*, of which there are three types: *visualizations*, *written tasks* and *actions* carried out in the external world. The techniques and procedures for inducing the trance-like states required for the *visualization tasks* are outlined in *Chapter 3*.

The procedure has been written using the more vernacular second person "you" form, as if addressing the reader using the book as a self-help manual. Practitioners will naturally use the same language with their clients.

Session number, frequency, duration and location

As a general rule, each step corresponds to a single session and each session lasts between fifty and seventy-five minutes. However, every individual and practitioner is unique, and some steps may overlap, their order may change and the time attributed to each may vary. Some steps may be omitted altogether. I usually begin with the following order in mind and, if possible, try to stick to it.

Self-help

For those using the book as a *self-help guide*, I suggest using the same location for every session. Choose a place where no-one is going to disturb you, and make potential visitors aware of your need for privacy. You could put a note on the door to that effect. Set aside an allotted time and day, for example between seven and eight on Tuesdays and Thursdays. Respect these time boundaries, as you would respect those agreed with a practitioner. Setting these boundaries and keeping to them is part of the therapeutic process and a key tool in the process of change. Bear in mind that over-running your session entails breaking a boundary.

Practitioners

In my experience, the procedure usually requires eight sessions. One for each step and an introductory session. As with any short term solution focused model, the client expects to be given a specific time frame. I attempt to negotiate an initial commitment of seven sessions with a maximum of two subsequent sessions if required.

With regards to the duration of the session, I personally advocate an hourly session, or even a seventy-five minute session. Many practitioners prefer to maintain the fifty minute therapeutic hour. There are numerous arguments both for and against both these approaches. In my view, what matters is that whatever time boundaries are agreed upon, they are maintained.

The *written task* questions should be asked verbally during the session. Those *written tasks* that involve writing a story can be either given as additional homework or the story can be elicited verbally during the session.

Effectiveness

The interventions that make up the *Safe Space* procedure are not magical cures, though they can sometimes work like magical cures. Nevertheless, it is a good policy to treat the procedure like any other exercise, where constancy and focus are essential in order to achieve the desired goal. Keep your aspirations realistic. Anxiety and panic can never completely be overcome as they are natural and, at times, essential to our survival. As long as you reverse the downward spiral of anxiety and panic, each day and each experience will nudge you along the road to a more fulfilling and anxiety free world.

Procedure content

w = written task   v = visualization   a = action

Introducing the procedure

Self-help

The previous chapters in this book serve as introduction to the procedure.

Notes for practitioners

Sharing the theory and procedure with the client is one way of enabling the client to determine more effectively their own healing process. The information can either be introduced in totality at the beginning of the process, or provided in segments at the beginning of each *step* or session. The amount of information you provide will naturally depend upon your client's needs and on your personal preference.

The following introduction is most effective when carried out in the first session.

1.) *Elicit when the client feels anxious and what they think causes it.*

2.) *Introduce the concept of selves*

The aim here is to communicate the idea that it is possible to feel different ways about the same things at the same time. For example, the desire to stay in bed in the morning and the need to get up and go to work.

Introduce the notion of *semi-autonomous selves.*

3.) *Introduce the idea of a child self and core feeling*

The aim here is to identify the *self* that experiences the anxiety and panic. Associate this *self* with the term *Child self.*

4.) *Introduce the idea of a Parent self*

The aim here is to identify times when the client has felt confident and in control. Associate this *self* with the term *Parent self.*

5.) *Introduce the idea of a Protector self*

Elicit how the client tends to defend themselves against potential threats and associate this *self* with term *Protector.* The list of *Protective strategies* in *Chapter 2* can be used as a prompt in this task.

6.) *Introduce the idea of an originating event.*
Elicit, if possible, the cause of the client's anxiety/panic and associate it with the term *originating event.*

7.) *Provide the procedure*
Explain how the procedure aims to empower the client to overcome their anxiety/panic in the following three ways:

1. By changing the client's relationship to the *originating event.*
2. By reinforcing the resources of the *parent self.*
3. By training the *protector* to respond appropriately to prevailing circumstances.

8.) *Introduce the role of visualizations and alley fears*
Relay how some of the *tasks* involve *visualizations* which are most effectively carried out in a trance-like state. Allay any fears the client may have about hypnosis. A list of common misconceptions can be found in the section, *Myths and facts about hypnosis* in *Chapter 3.*

Step 1
The Present

Step 1 has 3 *parts*. In *part 1* you identify your situation as you see it now, and how you want it to change. In *Part 2* you describe what happens to trigger your symptoms. In *Part 3* you explore any reasons you may have had for not changing till now.

Part 1: Where I am now

Your first and only *task* in this *part* is to express as simply and as briefly as you can your situation as you see it now, how you think you came to be here, and where you would like to be.

Task 1: Your overview

Instructions

Answer the questions in the left hand column. The right hand column contains prompts and examples. There are no right and wrong answers to the questions though, were you to re-read your answers at the end of the process, you may discover that you would wish to modify or add to them. The aim here is not to answer the questions correctly, but for you to describe your situation as you see it now. Attempt to make your answers as short and concise as you can.

Written Task

My overview	Prompts & examples
1. What do I *feel* that I don't want to feel and when does this feeling occur?	*e.g. I feel anxious before interviews, among strangers, when speaking in public.*
2. How would I like my experience to be?	*Think of a scenario and imagine how you would wish to behave.*

My overview	Prompts & examples
3. What do I think originally caused my anxiety or panic?	*Write down the first time you remember feeling anxiety or panic.*
4. What prompted me to decide to overcome my anxiety or panic?	*e.g. an event that recently occurred, present circumstances or particular upcoming event.*

Part 2 : My *old story*

This *part* involves describing, in the form of a story, what happens to trigger your anxiety and panic. Your story is referred to here as your *old story* and focuses on the details and the specifics of what happens. There are 3 *tasks* in this *part,* all of which are *written tasks.*

Most of you are very aware of when, where and with whom you become anxious or panicky. Writing down what you know in the form of a *story* offers you the opportunity to see how your mood changes from a new perspective. Sometimes, simply remembering or thinking about how and when we experience anxiety or panic often triggers similar, milder feelings. If this is the case, experiencing these milder feelings in a safe, controlled environment is a good opportunity for you to really observe your feelings. Your *old story* will also be used at the end of the procedure as a way of confirming that change has taken place.

One way of writing your *old story* is to treat it as if you were making a short documentary or film. The more details the film contains, the more "realistic" it will seem.

Task 1: Your *old story notes*

Instructions

This task is a note making exercise that prepares you for writing your *old story narrative.* As in *Part 1*, complete the left hand column, using the prompts in the right hand column to guide you. Every detail helps. Once you have answered a question, try to follow it up with the question, *what else?* For example, if you are describing a certain stretch of road, ask yourself what makes it different from other stretches of road? Are there any bridges? Are there lots of cars or only a few? Does it have a slip road or an exit? In those cases when your anxiety or panic is triggered by something you experience regularly, next time you experience it, try to make a mental note of your surroundings and feelings. Such a task may seem difficult, but can in itself be therapeutic as you are effectively reframing your experience.

When carrying out the *task*, it is worth bearing in mind two things: Firstly, the circumstances that trigger anxiety and panic are not necessarily directly related to those circumstances that originally caused them. Secondly, your ultimate aim of the *Safe Space* procedure is not to change the external world or to manage your symptoms, but rather to shift your relationship to the cause of your anxiety so that external events and triggers no longer have the same effect.

Written Task

My *old story notes*	**Prompts & examples**
1. Script title	*Think of a recent event that caused you to feel anxious or panicky. Give this event a title or describe it using one sentence. e.g. "The interview"*
2. When and where does my story take place?	*e.g. a particular place, time of day, month, season, occasion.*
3. How long does my story last?	*Treat the beginning as just before you begin to feel anxiety or panic and the end when the feeling has passed.*
4. What can I see, hear, smell, taste?	*Describe the scene in as much detail as possible.*

My *old story notes continued*	**Prompts & examples**
5. Who am I with, if anybody?	*Does being with certain people, or groups of people make a difference? For example strangers, partners, people with certain roles, jobs or positions. If so, who are these people?*
6. How do I feel?	

	Likelihood of symptom 0-10	Intensity highest 0-10	Intensity now 0-10
Increased heart rate			
Quicker breathing			
Desire to run			
Desire to attack			
Grinding teeth			
Forgetfulness			
Clumsiness			
Picking at food			
Sweating			
Shaking			
Obsessive tidying			
Impatient			
Shaky voice			
Nervous tick			
Time anxiety			

The likelihood of a symptom refers to when you are experiencing anxiety and panic. The greater the likelihood and intensity, the higher the number.

7. What would someone else watching me see?	*How would someone know you were anxious or panicky? For example, would you move or speak differently?*

Task 2: Your *old story narrative*

By narrating your experience in the form of a story you are effectively reframing the events in a way that shifts your relationship to them. Your *old story* will also be used at the end of the procedure to confirm that change has taken place.

Instructions

Your *old story narrative* is based on your *old story notes.* Write your *old story* using the past tense and using the third person "he" or "she", as if you were watching yourself act out the scene. Use the same title you chose in your *old script notes.* Start the story before your anxiety begins and finish when the anxiety has passed.

Example: Sam's *old story narrative*

The following example is an extract from Sam's interview experience.

Title: The Interview

Yesterday was the day of Sam's interview. He had set his alarm to wake him at dawn. Ring Ring Ring! Sam woke up enveloped by fear of a forgotten dream. His partner, Liz, stirred beside him.

"What time is it?" she asked.

"It's still early. Go back to sleep." Sam replied, not mentioning to her that it was three hours before he had to get up. Sam closed his eyes, worried about falling back to sleep and fell back to sleep. He woke up again at a quarter to eight, panicked, scrambled out of bed and into the bathroom. Only fifteen minutes left before he had to leave. After cutting himself shaving, he slipped on the shirt he had ironed the previous evening and fumbled with the buttons. He checked himself in the mirror, tore the shirts off and rummaged in the wardrobe for another one.

[Your *Old story narrative* overleaf]

Written Task

My *old story narrative*

Title:

Narrative:

Task 3: Your *old story optional note*

This *task* is optional. Its goal is to enable you to increase your self awareness and to focus your intention on the resources you have at your disposal.

Instructions

Answer as many of the questions below as you can.

Written Task

My *old story optional notes*	**prompts & examples**
1. When do the *triggers* seem to affect me most?	*e.g. when you are tired, at specific times of day, on specific occasions.*
2. How is life different because of my anxiety/panic?	*e.g. specific things you cannot do, places you cannot go to, people you cannot bond with, potential you cannot reach, goals you cannot achieve.*
5. What solutions have I tried? How effective were they and for how long?	*e.g. medication, counselling, hypnosis, stress management.*
6. How will I know when I have solved the problem?	*i.e. what would you be doing, saying, wearing differently?*
7. What makes things better?	*e.g. not being stressed or tired, stability in relationships or at work, something to look forward to, success at work, certain people or events.*
8. What makes things worse?	*e.g. being tired, instability in relationships, certain people or events.*

My *old story optional notes* continued	**prompts & examples**
9. When do I *not* feel anxious or panicky? What is different?	*i.e. is it because certain people or circumstances are absent or because they are present?*
10. In what situations do I cope well that others may feel anxious about?	*e.g. travelling by air, meeting new people, competitive sports, multi-tasking.*
11. When have I felt really good and when everything is going well.	*e.g. a particular time at work, with a person, while practicing a sport, while creating something.*
12. What, if anything, makes it more difficult for me to achieve my goal?	*e.g. a particular person or set of circumstances.*
13. When have I had a problem and managed to overcome it. How did I overcome it?	
14. What do I consider my strengths to be?	*e.g. patience, imagination, consistency, keeping focused, hard working, being committed, being trustworthy, perceptiveness, being humble.*
15. Who else, if anyone, wants me to overcome my anxiety or panic, and why?	
16. Who do I admire most and why?	*The person can be dead or alive, real or fictitious.*
17. Who, if anybody, is supporting me and how?	*e.g. friends, family, professionals, work colleagues.*
18. Who do I know, if anyone, who experiences anxiety or panic? How do I think they deal with it?	

Part 3: Why I am still here

It is possible that there are very good reasons for not changing. Indeed, you may gain something by not changing. That someone should imply that you have a vested interest in suffering from anxiety and panic may seem odd, or slightly insulting even. Entertaining this idea, however, can create an important positive shift in your relationship to the problem.

One of the most obvious gains of experiencing anxiety or panic is that it gives you a reason to avoid those feelings you fear most. For example, Sam's anxiety that was triggered by interviews gave Sam a good reason to avoid the possibility of being humiliated in public – one of his greatest fears. Likewise, Sam's anxiety about committing himself to a long term relationship meant that he never got involved enough to feel the pain caused by what he considered to be an inevitable rejection and betrayal. Another example is that of the man who panicked every time someone "stole" his parking space. By focusing his attention on "trespassers" he had found a far more controllable way of expressing his feelings of anger and shame that originated from a sexual abuse in infancy.

One could argue that the above gains are not really gains at all in that they do not give us pleasure, but simply enable us to avoid pain and protect our self-esteem. Other gains do exist, however, that actively bolster our self-esteem. *Motivation* is one of these. For example, Sam's fear of being humiliated in public motivated him to improve his sports abilities and consequently he gained respect and admiration from his opponents.

Another thing we gain by identifying with a problem such as anxiety and panic is the formation of a *world view* that allows us to understand the world and ourselves in a way that suggests our fears are logical and rational. For example, Sam's *world view* included the belief that all relationships ended in betrayal and that women, therefore, could not be trusted. This view of women gave Sam adequate reason to avoid committing to relationships and to justify his own betrayals. Likewise, Sam's belief that all recognized academics could only think "inside the box" provided Sam with a reason to feel okay about his own lack of a formal education.

Regardless of which *world view* we adhere to, when they are engrained into our psyche they provide us with a solid foundation on which to construct a reality in which we feel comfortable and secure. Sometimes, in fact, our *word views* become so engrained that the words *I believe* and *I think* are substituted for *I know*.

Our anxieties can, then, provide us with two significant gains: *Motivation* to enhance our abilities and skills, and a *world view* that enables us to understand an otherwise complex and often contradictory world.

Task 1: What you gain by not changing

This *task* prompts you to identify those things you gain by having your symptoms. The objective of this *task* is to shift your relationship to your problem and to help you find other ways of getting the same needs met, thus eradicating one of the impediments to overcoming your anxiety or panic.

Instructions

It is my experience that all of us, at some level, gain something by having a problem. For those of you who think you may, either complete this task now by answering the following questions, or simply slot the questions away in your mind to reflect on at your convenience. Whatever the case, when you do realize what it is that you gain, make sure that you complete the written task below.

Written Task

What I gain by not changing	Prompts & examples
a. Motivation to do the following:	*This is often something that will ultimately provide you with self-esteem, acknowledgement and respect.*
b. The following skills:	*e.g. particular social skills and abilities.*
c. A world view that includes the following beliefs:	*i.e. beliefs that serve to justify your fears.*

Task 2: What you risk losing if you change

If it is possible for you to gain something by having a problem, it is also possible that, were you to overcome the problem, you risk losing what you gained. When Sam, for example, changed his *world view* belief from, *women cannot be trusted* to *I find it difficult to trust women*, Sam could no longer blame his own betrayals on someone else. Likewise, by changing his belief that *academics cannot think outside the box* to *I find it difficult to learn from others* meant that he could no longer ignore his fear.

By overcoming a problem, you could also lose those things that have been determined by having the problem. For example, if your anxiety is triggered by driving at speed, you may have been prompted to acquire a car that doesn't go very fast. Were you to overcome your fear triggered by speed, you may want to trade your car in for something a little zippier. Likewise, if you were to overcome an anxiety triggered by flying, you may wish to substitute a holiday plan to somewhere with a two hundred mile radius, to a location a little more exotic and further afield.

Changing cars and travel routes, though, is unlikely to be reason enough to cling onto a problem, especially when the new alternative is likely to be more rewarding. However, it is not just our relationship to objects and plans that can be affected. Our relationship to people can be too. Just as overcoming anxiety triggered by driving at speed may prompt us to purchase a car that fulfils our desires rather than cater for our needs, so it is with people. For example, a woman who has a driving related anxiety may also have a husband who likes to be "behind the wheel". Were the woman to overcome her fear of driving, she may be more inclined to want to drive when her husband is in the car, subtly altering the status quo in the relationship. If her husband does not want to change, there is the potential for conflict.

An example of this is that of a client of mine called Mary who became anxious and panicky when forced into making decisions. This was partly due to her experience as a child of having to take responsibility for the household cooking and shopping, and of being severely chastised by her parents when, in their eyes, she invariably did everything wrong. Mary later married a man who thrived on making decisions and on taking responsibility for them and, inevitably, Mary found herself becoming increasingly dependent on him. Their relationship resembled that of a daughter-father relationship. When Mary began to overcome her anxiety she began to make her own decisions, one of which was to begin working. Her husband found this change difficult to adjust to, perhaps because his own need of being needed was no longer adequately being met. Although the husband initially tried to block Mary's progress, and Mary risked jeopardising what had been an otherwise harmonious, if perhaps restricted, relationship, she did not give up her intention to work. Mary finally did begin work and the last I heard was that both she and her husband both feel they have a more fulfilling and rewarding relationship.

With change, then, comes risk, but also the opportunity of gaining something better.

Instructions

Complete the left hand column.

Written Task

What I affect by overcoming my problem	Prompts & examples
a. My world view	*What beliefs would you change?*
b. Things I own or skills I use	*What "things" or skills may you no longer need? e.g. slow car, restricted travel plans, a particular way of dressing, a particular way of behaving.*
c. Relationships	*Who will be most affected by you change? How would overcoming your anxiety improve your relationship with them?*

What if you are overwhelmed by your feelings?

This section does not contain a *task* but prompts you to reflect on other possible barriers to positive change. One of these may be the belief that to overcome your anxieties you must confront your fears, and thus be forced to re-experience those feelings you dread most. Sam equated this fear to the act of jumping headfirst into a dark, bottomless well from which he would be unable to climb back out.

Another less abstract example of this *fear of fear* was offered to me by a sixteen year client called Deborah who came to see me because of her fear of spiders. Although spiders are harmless creatures, certainly in Britain, I would never underestimate how powerful and overwhelming fears can be. However, the following story Deborah recounted illustrates very well how the *fear of fear* can be more debilitating than the thing feared.

Deborah's story took place at a friend's house. They were watching television together when Deborah's friend told her that she had glimpsed a spider disappear behind the cushion next to her. Deborah may not have actually seen the spider, but the idea that there was one there was enough to make her jump up and scream. As Deborah recounted this part of the story, her breathing noticeably quickened. However, when she recounted the part of the story when the spider emerged from behind the cushion, Deborah's breathing slowed down perceptibly. In other words, once she was able to monitor what it was she feared, her fear decreased because she was in a position to respond accordingly. She could see what she feared and could therefore either keep at a safe distance away, kill it, catch it or even grow used to or like it. It was only when Deborah couldn't see the spider that she felt panicky and out of control.

The following story of Sally really highlights the notion that fear is often purely in the mind. Sally, for reasons of her own, felt too frightened to leave her house unaccompanied. So skilled had she become at making sure she would not be forced to venture out alone that, on the bitterly cold January morning she visited me for the first time, she arrived by taxi with no shoes on, offering the excuse that she had forgotten them in the taxi. During the session, I agreed with Sally to do a role play with a teddy bear she had brought along. In the role play, Sally took the part of a parent, and the teddy bear took the part of Sally's needy and fearful *self*. I then agreed with Sally that she put the teddy bear as far away from herself as she felt comfortable with, and to leave it there for thirty seconds. Sally was perfectly capable of understanding that the teddy bear was not her needy *self*, yet she was only able to place the teddy bear a few feet away and to leave it there for no more than a few seconds. Sally repeated this exercise for the whole session, progressively increasing the distance and the time. She managed to add on a few feet and a few seconds. Just before the session ended I handed Sally her coat and, prompted by a CD that fell out of her pocket, asked Sally who her favourite singer was. As Sally reeled off a whole list of pop artists, I accompanied her to the door where a friend of Sally's was waiting to collect her, proffering a pair of trainers. I watched Sally as she made her way down the pavement without her teddy. This story shows how some fears that seem to be engrained into the very fabric of our psychological make-up are often more easily shed than we think.

The aim of the procedure in this book is not to progressively come to tolerate feelings by reframing or habitualizing ourselves to them, as was the case with Sally. Rather, it is to develop a relationship between the part of us that can cope (the *parent self*), and the part that, for whatever reason, has been unable to cope in the past (the *child self*). There may be times, however, that we experience anxiety and panic so intensely, that it renders our ability to *parent* ourselves virtually impossible? We are effectively "out of control".

Being in control of your emotions

This brings us to the notion of "being in control". For many who experience anxiety or panic, no matter how much the *parent self* wants to look after the *child self* , the idea of "going down the well" or "taking the cushion away" can be a pretty frightening one. We often suspect that dark and dreadful feelings will bob to the surface and be revealed, and we feel a natural impulse to want to control them by either repressing them or denying them.

An architect client of mine called Nick used an eloquent analogy to describe the way he tried, unsuccessfully, to repress his feelings. He described how he had built a "dam wall which he had constructed out of his propensity to rationalise everything. In his analogy, the water represented his emotions and the dam wall represented his rational self. So much "water" accumulated, though, that it was inevitable that the dam would eventually burst. Nick was so terrified of this happening that he obsessively tapped up even the tiniest of leaks, effectively repressing almost every emotion. The accumulation of these repressed feelings only served to increase the pressure on the dam wall. Nick, not surprisingly, suffered from all kinds of psychosomatic illnesses, including mild depression.

The notion of *being in control* is not, then to fortify the "dam wall", but to let the feelings "flow" in a way that we feel comfortable with. In other words, in a way that does not feel overwhelming. Alternatively, our emotions are blocked, our life is lacklustre and our connection with other people severely limited. The notion of *being in control* refers, then, to the idea of being able to allow our feelings to flow, and of being able to determine how, when, to what extent and where this happens.

In control of change

Being *in control* of creating change implies that we have decided to take responsibility for our actions and reactions. This may seem nothing new in that, as adults, we are automatically responsible for our actions. However, one of the greatest barriers to change is the notion that someone or something else such as a parent, an accident, an abuser or simply bad luck are to blame for our anxiety and panic, and therefore responsible for the way we respond. Or rather, that our actions and behaviour are a direct response to these. By taking control of how we feel, we are effectively taking on the responsibility for everything we do and say. In other words, we are no longer a victim, nor do we engineer situations which suggest we are victims.

Overview

In this chapter we have entertained the notion that there are things we gain by not changing, and things we can lose by changing. It also reflects on how fear of the feelings we associate with change can immobilise us.

However, although we may fear change, everyone has a natural desire to strive towards perfection. We may never reach this ideal state, but inherent in all of us seems to be a force that impels us to evolve. So much so that, no matter how much we try to avoid certain events and feelings, we nearly always find ourselves embroiled in them, either because we re-create them ourselves or because we are drawn towards them. We may not be aware we are doing this, but our unconscious mind seems to force us to repeat the same patterns over and over again until the initial traumatic ending is resolved and we can move on. Sam, for example, always found himself in relationships in which another dominant male threatened to "steal" his partner. By replaying this *old story* he could, on the one hand, justify his world view that all women are likely betrayers, and on the other hand, attempt to change the original story by arriving at a happy ending. Whatever the case, there seems to be an inherent desire in everyone to evolve. It is this same desire that has brought you to this book and, in the case that you are a practitioner, that brings your clients to you.

Everybody, in my experience is capable of change, even if these changes are imperceptible, and for those of us who choose not to control change, sooner or later change will invariably be forced upon us.

The next step

Ironically perhaps, it is often the case that when we *do* decide to take control of change is when we meet the most resistance, simply because the risks become more "real". This tendency to put off taking the final step is often due to a last defiant gasp of an angry *child self*, or by a desire to hang on to an *old story* which, although evidently detrimental to our happiness, is something we are familiar with and skilled at. Other reasons for not taking the next step may include a newly formed conviction that you actually feel okay now and therefore do not need to change, or the belief that some other extremely pressing matter must take priority. The challenge of forging a new path is to be aware of this natural tendency to want to take the old one. It may require a little push or a leap of faith. Or maybe it won't.

Step 2
A Possible Future

In *Step 1* you focused your attention on your *old story* and on how you don't want to feel. *Part 2* focuses on how to create your *new story* and on how you *do* want to feel.

There are *2 parts* to this *step*. *Part 1* provides an analogy that offers a new perspective on your *old story* and a means of achieving an alternative ending. *Part 2* uses a *what if* scenario that enables you to visualize what your future might be like were you to have overcome your anxiety.

Part 1: How to change my *old story*

Let's return to the *Family Analogy* included in the first chapter. The following version provides you with a similar way of understanding the dynamics of anxiety and panic by representing them in terms of a family crisis. In the analogy, the mother and father represent the male and female *parent selves*, the child represents the *child self* and the pet dog represents the *protector*.

Task 1: The Family Analogy

The *Family Analogy* has two scenes: *Scene 1: The problem* and *Scene 2: The solution.*

Instructions

Read the analogy, circle the boxed responses you think most likely and number them in the order you feel is most appropriate.

> **Scene 1 : The problem**
> Imagine a dog. It can be big or small, scruffy or groomed, fat or lean, or somewhere in between. It can have black fur, white fur or brown fur, be spotted or patched. Its bark may be a shrill yap or a growling grunt. Whatever dog comes to mind, in this story, its name is *Woof.*

Woof lives in a two story house with a front door that leads to the street and a back door that leads to a garden shed. The house, just like *Woof*, can be whatever you imagine it to be. It can be a modern suburban property, an old rickety mansion, a thatched cottage or a modest end of terrace abode.

The house is also inhabited by seven year old Lolita, her father, Tom, and her mother, Suzi. *Woof* , their very loyal pet has an extremely acute sense of hearing and smell which tends to set him off barking at the slightest provocation. In fact, so loyal and sensitive is *Woof* that he is a little over zealous in his desire to warn his family of potential threats, even when he is seemingly sound asleep and curled up on his mat, as is the case this afternoon when someone knocks at the door.

Knock, knock, knock.

Woof's ears prick up and instinctively he barks to alert Tom and Suzie of the "intruder". *Woof woof woof*, he barks. But neither Tom nor Suzi respond to his warning. Instead, whoever is at the door knocks a little harder, *KNOCK KNOCK KNOCK,* and *Woof* barks a little louder too, *WOOF WOOF WOOF.*

Still, neither Tom nor Suzi appear. *Woof* jumps up from his mat, races towards the front door and leaps up at it, *WOOF WOOF* WOOF. It is at this point that little seven years old Lolita appears at the top of the stairs and sees *Woof* leaping and barking at the door.

Written Task

Predicted reactions

What do you think little Lolita does?

Circle the responses you think most likely and number them in the order you feel most appropriate.

Does Lolita...

1. go downstairs and answer the door?	Yes No
2. try to calm *Woof* down?	Yes No
3. call out for mummy and daddy	Yes No
4. look for mummy and daddy	Yes No
5. start crying	Yes No
6. hide under the bed	Yes No

Assuming you have chosen the most common responses, you will have likely circled *Yes* for numbers 3, 4, 5 or 6. If you haven't, let's add to the story that little Lolita goes to look for mummy and daddy but can't find them anywhere in the house. Let's also say that this is the first time little Lolita has found herself alone in the house. Taking into consideration these additions to the story, let's assume that you have not chosen the option of little Lolita answering the front door.

Scene 2: The solution

What little Lolita doesn't know is that her parents absence is due to a miscommunication between the two of them. Just before the arrival of whoever had knocked at the door, her mother, Suzi, had nipped out to ask the next door neighbour for some milk, and her father, Tom, had popped out to the garden shed for something or other. On their way out, both had called out to the other to say what they were doing, but neither had heard one another. Both believed that little Lolita was in the care of the other.

If we were to go forward in time to when Lolita's mother returned to the house to find *Woof* frantically running around barking and no sign of little Lolita, she may respond in a variety of ways. In the case that it was Lolita's father who arrived first, he may respond in the same way or in a different way.

Written Task

Predicted solutions

1. In which order do you think little Lolita's mother and father would likely respond?
   Number them in sequence. Add your own responses if you wish.

	Mother	Father
Try to ascertain what was causing *Woof* to bark.		
Try to calm *Woof* down.		
Look for Lolita.		
Try to comfort Lolita.		
Try to ascertain from little Lolita what had happened.		
Look for your partner and blame him/her.		
Check for evidence of intruders in the house.		

Predicted solutions continued

2. Do you think that Lolita's experience of her parents being absent in the house would influence how she felt if someone were to knock on the door the next day? If so, do you predict that her anxiety level would...

    a) increase
    b) decrease
    c) remain the same

3. If one or both of Lolita's parents had been at home when there was a knock on the door, which of the following do you think they would have done and in what order?

    1. Answer door.
    2. Let her parents answer the door.
    3. Tell Woof to stop barking.

4. If at least one of her parents had been home to answer the door and to calm *Woof* down, if someone were to knock on the door the next day, do you predict that her anxiety level would...

    a) increase
    b) decrease
    c) remain the same

5. Of which do you think little Lolita was more frightened?

    a) the knocking at the door
    b) her parents not being there to answer the door?

6. If you discovered that it was customary for Lolita to find herself alone in the house, which of the following would you suggest to Lolita's parents?

Choose one option.

1. That Lolita learn to control her fear and answer the door.
2. That the parents allow the dog to deal with the intruder.
3. For Lolita's parents to ensure they are always available.

With regards to question six, the first of the three options may appear rather harsh considering Lolita's age. The second option may appear ludicrous. However, it is not uncommon for those of us who suffer from anxiety and panic to attempt to control our fears. Nor it is uncommon that we rely on protective instincts to deal with threats. And once we empower our instincts in this way, it becomes increasingly difficult to control them, just as it becomes more difficult to teach an old dog new tricks.

Certainly, controlling our fears and relying solely on our *protector* are unlikely long term solutions. If you agree they are not, and have therefore chosen as a solution that of Lolita's parents ensuring that they are always available, then this procedure is designed specifically for you.

Whatever options you have chosen, the presence or absence of Lolita's parents influences Lolita's sense of safety and thus how she responds. When Lolita's parents are absent, she feels unsafe and when they are present, she feels safer because parents can do things Lolita cannot. For example, they can call on a wealth of experience to analyse situations, take decisions and respond appropriately in order to keep Lolita safe.

At the risk of stating the obvious, then, it is Lolita's parent's *(parent self)* who are responsible for providing Lolita *(child self)* with a safe environment within which she can grow and explore. If this does not happen, Lolita will be forced to fend for herself either by attempting to acquire more quickly the resources of her parents, or by allowing the dog (her *protector)* to take control – a useful short term solution, but rarely beneficial in the long term. In conclusion, a person will behave according to the resources they have at their disposal, and their instincts, if not trained, will respond without too much pre-planning and conscious analysis.

Introducing trauma into the analogy

In the *Family Analogy*, a harmless visitor knocks on the door while Lolita's parents are out. It is hardly an event that would induce significant trauma. If, however, the person knocking on the door had done something to traumatise Lolita, it would be natural for similar future scenarios to trigger anxiety in Lolita. For example, let's imagine that the person knocking at the door had been a burglar who, assuming that nobody was at home, broke into the house and stole all Lolita's toys. Were Lolita to have witnessed this event, it is likely that future scenarios in which someone knocks on the door in a similar fashion and at a similar time would prompt Lolita's anxiety levels to rise. And in the case that the burglar had badly beaten the dog, the dog would likely be even more sensitive to the sound of knocking on the door.

Future triggers for both Lolita and the dog could include the type clothes the burglar was wearing, the time of day, a particular film Lolita was watching at the time, the smell of the burglar's aftershave.

If Lolita's parents had been in the house but unable to deal with the threat, either because they were too frightened, drunk, drugged, or simply because the burglar was armed and dangerous, it may be that Lolita would respond in a similar way.

If, on the other hand, the parents were present and able to repel the burglar, the experience may have caused Lolita to feel anxious, but the fact that her parents were able to deal with the threat would have fostered a sense of trust in her parents and, thus, in the world and her future.

Conclusion

In the *Family Analogy* the protagonists represent our *internal family of selves*. The *parents* represent our adult resources and skills, the child Lolita represents our emotions and feelings, and *Woof* represents our instincts and protective strategies. If we were to treat our *internal family of selves* in the same way, by applying the same solutions, the most suitable course of action would be to make sure that we effectively *parent* our *child* in order that it feels safe, and that we train our *protector* to respond appropriately and in accordance with the *parent self's* wishes.

Part 2: How my *new story* might be

In this *part* a *what if* scenario enables you to visualize what your future might be like were you to have overcome your anxiety. The *task* can be carried out as both a *written task* and a *visualization*. Whether you choose to carry out one or both, your following *miracle new story notes* will serve as preparation.

Task 1: Your *miracle new story* notes

What if, while you were asleep a miracle took place which meant that when you woke up you no longer suffered from anxiety or panic?

How the miracle occurred does not matter. If you hold strong spiritual or religious beliefs, perhaps an angel, spirit or light being visited you in a dream. If you are an atheist or pragmatist, maybe it was a chance electrical charge. If you have a vivid imagination or are a computer enthusiast, it could be a virtual world that your alter ego awakes in. Whatever your beliefs or inclinations, it doesn't really make any difference. The miracle occurred while you were asleep, and when you wake up you have no recollection of what happened. All you are aware of is that something has shifted inside and, because of this shift, you behave as someone who does not suffer from anxiety or panic. And other people notice this shift too.

Instructions

Answer the following questions:

Written Task

My *miracle new story* notes	**Prompts & examples**
When you wake up in the morning after the "miracle" has occurred.....	
1. What would be the first clue that something has changed?	*e.g. you feel calmer, you get up more quickly or more slowly.*
2. How would others notice I am different?	*e.g. you are more or less talkative.*
3. How would I walk and talk differently?	*e.g. more purposefully*
4. What would I wear that is different?	*e.g. brighter or darker colours, smarter or more causal.*
5. How would I feel?	*e.g. less stressed, more inclined to play.*
6. What would I notice about my energy levels?	*e.g. higher or lower.*
7. How would I respond to people differently?	*e.g. more thoughtfully*
8. How would people respond differently to me?	*e.g. more enthusiastically*
9. How would my life be different because of the change?	*e.g. better personal*

Task 2: Your *miracle new story* narrative

This *task* involves writing a short story which begins with you waking up in the morning after the "miracle" has taken place.

Instructions

Write your story using the third person "he" or "she", and in the present tense, as if it were happening now. For example, *he gets up at eight o'clock*. Be as realistic or as inventive as you wish.

Example

Sam started his *Miracle new story narrative* in the following way.

> **Sam's miracle new story**
>
> Today is the day of Sam's interview. He had not set the alarm, trusting in his body to wake him up at the right time. When he does wake up, he feels strangely alive, the warm optimism of a forgotten dream curled up inside him. Liz, his partner, stirs beside him.
>
> "What time is it?" she asks.
>
> Sam looks at the clock. "Eight," he said, jumping out of bed, "fancy some breakfast?"
>
> Liz looks at him suspiciously." Are you alright?" she asks, expecting Sam to snap back. He did not. He just grins and slopes off into the bathroom. When he reappears he slips on the shirt he ironed the previous evening and smiles at himself in the mirror.

Written Task

My *miracle new story* narrative

Task 3: Your *Miracle new story* visualization

Your *miracle new story visualization* runs along the same lines as the narrative.

Instructions

Read the following procedure until it is firmly embedded in your memory. If you are using the book as a self-help manual, use the procedure for inducing a light trance outlined in the *Safe Space procedure for self-hypnosis* in *Chapter 3.* If you are inducing trance in a client use the *Safe Space procedure for hypnosis* outlined in the same chapter. This *visualization* does not require the anchoring of a *special place.*

Visualization

My *miracle new story* visualization

1. Trance induction

Preparation - outside – eyes closed - inside – small things – different things – transforming things – in control of holding on – in control of letting go – counting down from ten to zero.

2. Task

As you count down from ten to zero, say to yourself *A miracle has occurred and I am about to see myself wake up in my room no longer suffering from anxiety.*

When you reach zero, imagine yourself looking into the room that your *future self* is waking up in. Notice how differently this future self looks and behaves. If there are other people in the room, notice how they respond differently.

3. Awakener

Counting up from one to ten – eyes open

The next step

This *step* has focused on what it is that needs to change in your *old story* in order to achieve an anxiety free *new story* and how this *new story* might feel. The next *step* focuses your attention on the origin of your anxiety or panic.

Step 3
The Past

This *step* focuses on the original cause of your anxiety and on the feelings this event caused. The purpose of this *step* is not to relive the experience, but to lay the groundwork for *step 5* in which you change the way you relate to this experience.

This *step has* two parts. In *Part 1* you identify the event or set of circumstances that lie at the root of your anxiety. In *Part 2* you identify the feelings you associate with this event.

Part 1: How my *old story* began

The cause of your anxiety, referred to here as your *originating event*, is the "blue print" for your *old script.* Most people have a good idea as to what this *originating event* is. Others, however, may be uncertain. This may be because the *originating event* occurred such a long time ago that you simply don't remember. It may be that you have re-enacted the *story* so many times that you cannot isolate any one particular episode. Or it may be that the *originating event* did not actually trigger the symptoms, but that a later comparatively insignificant event did.

Another factor that can hinder identifying the *originating event* is that it may seem to be unrelated to the triggers. For example, the *originating event* of the woman who felt anxious when driving through one-way systems bridges turned out to be an acrimonious separation from his wife and children coupled with the daunting prospect of a life without them. Another example is that of the man whose anxiety was triggered by people trespassing on his car parking space, the *originating event* of which was a sexual abuse.

It may also be that the *originating event* was so traumatic that the unconscious mind, in order to protect you, impedes you from recalling it. If this is the case, of that the *originating event* occurred at such a young age that you cannot recall it, you may wish to consider employing a practitioner experienced in regression and uncovering techniques.

Alternative ways of uncovering your *originating event*

The following uncovering techniques are designed to enable you to determine with greater precision what your *originating event* is, or to confirm what you already suspect.

For those of you who have some clue as to the source of your anxiety but are not sure, some well formed questions aimed at identifying when, why and with whom your anxiety or panic manifests itself is usually sufficient in order to the link the clues to a past event.

For those of you who are uncertain about the source of your anxiety, as a basis for your search, you could explore the following themes, often referred to as the *seven psycho-dynamics of a symptom*. They include self sabotage, past experience, internal conflict, body symptoms, secondary gain, identification and imprint.

Self sabotage

If you are prone to self sabotage it could be that a past experience created a belief that defined your expectation of success. For example, the belief that to be loved you must be a winner. When we believe that change is beyond us, we often choose the familiar pain of the problem, for example failure, and blame it on someone or something else. Self sabotaging is often related to low self esteem.

Suggested avenues to explore: Incidents that had an impact on self esteem.

Past experience

A past event which was painful or incorrectly perceived or remembered by the unconscious is the most common and obvious cause. For example, an incident in which someone is attacked by a dog could be the cause of anxiety triggered by dogs.

Suggested avenues to explore: Incidents directly related to the triggers.

Internal conflict

When we experience anxiety and panic in conjunction with internal conflict, we often prevent ourselves from carrying out a desire that we consider taboo. For example, if we feel anxious or panicky around something we do secretly, there is often an issue around the subject of the secret.

Suggested avenues to explore: Incidents associated with guilt and shame.

Body symptoms
Body symptoms such as psychosomatic illnesses often give clues as to the cause of the problem. For example, skin disorders may relate to issues around intimacy. Naturally, it is difficult to distinguish between what is psychosomatic and what is not. However, simply entertaining the possibility that a symptom could be psychosomatic may provide some useful clues.
Suggested avenues to explore: Exploring connections between physical symptoms and feelings.

Secondary gain
When you gain or hope to gain something, such as attention, admiration or respect, the cause of the anxiety and panic may likely be connected to the desired gain.
Suggested avenues to explore: What you gain by having your anxiety.

Identification
Sometimes we identify with a hero or loved one who suffers from anxiety and panic. Exploring how we perceive this person's life may give us clues as to our own history.
Suggested avenues to explore: People we admire or associate with.

Imprint or attribution
An imprint is a belief that has been implanted into your mind, usually by an authority figure. For example, many parents tell their children that they are lazy in hope that this will motivate them. When the unconscious takes on board these beliefs, they can become deeply held.
Suggested avenues to explore: Any strong convictions or beliefs you hold.

If you cannot uncover your *originating event*

It is not paramount that you know your *originating event.* Any event you can remember in which your *old story* plays itself out will suffice. On this basis, even the most recent experience of anxiety and panic can be used as a substitute for an *originating event* as it contains the same plot and has the potential to prompt the same painful feelings. Naturally, if the "original" *originating event* is available, use it.

Regardless of whether you are using an *originating event*, or using a substitute *originating event*, the only requirement for the procedure to work is that you have an emotional relationship to it. In other words, if you were to re-experience the event you would feel anxious or panicky.

Alternatively, you could employ an experienced hypnotherapist to access your past using one of a variety of regression and uncovering techniques.

Summary

The event you choose to treat as your *originating event* can be any of the following.

1. The *originating event*, if you know or think you know what it is.
2. A subsequent *trigger event.*
3. The *old script* you identified in *Part 1*.

Task 1: Your *originating event narrative*

This *task* involves describing your *originating event* or substitute *originating event* in the form of a story.

Instructions

Write your *originating event narrative* using the past tense and refer to your younger self using the third person, as if you were talking about another part of you, e.g. *my seven-year-old self.*

If you cannot remember the details of the event, use your imagination to create them. If the *originating event* was particularly traumatic and you do not wish to describe the whole of it, narrate as much of the story as you can.

Example: Sam's originating event

Sam's following *originating event narrative* describes the classroom episode during which Sam experienced humiliation and shame when unable to recite the seven times table in front of his classmates.

> *Title: The seven times table*
> Seven year old Sam was sitting in his maths class next to his best friend, Roderick. Sam was wearing his blue and red school tie, had a haystack of blond hair and needed to go to the toilet. The maths teacher, Mr.Young, stood by the blackboard at the front of the class. His eyes scanned the class, finally resting their gaze on Veronica.

"Veronica," he finally said, "the eight times table, please."

Veronica wore glasses, stuttered, and wasn't very pretty. The students behind her began to giggle. Sam too stifled a giggle. His need to pee became more urgent. Veronica stood up, stuttered her way through the recitation and sat down.

Mr. Young's gaze scoured the class again, and rested on Sam.

"Sam," he said. "The seven times table, please."

The giggles were for Sam this time. His need to pee intensified.

"One times seven is seven," said Sam, attempting a smirk for his friends. "Two times seven is fourteen. Three times seven is...."

Sam's mind went blank.

"Twenty-one," he finally managed to say, taking great pains to not pee himself.

" Four times seven is..."

Mind blank again.

"Twenty-eight," he stuttered. Sam knew he wasn't going to make it. The giggles behind him got louder. Blood rushed to Sam's face.

"Five times seven is......"

Sam wet himself and just stood there.

"Sam?" said Mr. Young. Sam didn't reply. Mr. Young sighed, before finally asking another student to complete the recitation.

"David," he said. "Perhaps you would like to continue."

Sam sat down. David stood up and reeled off the numbers. "Five times seven is thirty-five. Six times seven is forty-two. Seven times seven is forty-nine."

Everyone, Sam felt, was staring at his crotch, and when the bell sounded for the end of class, he remained rooted to his seat.

"You coming!" said his friend Roderick.

"No, he isn't" answered Mr. Young. Roderick scuttled out of the room and loitered in the corridor. Sam thought of running but dismissed the idea.

"So Sam," Mr. Young began, "what was it you found so funny?"

"Nothing, Sir," replied Sam.

"Nothing? What about this? Do you find this funny?" Mr. Young held a badge out in front of him with the number seven on it.

Sam looked at the badge blankly.

"You will wear it," continued Mr. Young, "until you are capable of reciting the seven times table. Is that understood?"

Sam's hands remained glued to his crutch.

"Well boy, take the badge!"

"Yes, sir," said Sam and took the badge, revealing his yellow shame.

Written Task

My *originating event narrative*

Title:

Part 2: My *feared feeling*

Your *feared feeling*, as defined in this book, is the emotion you experienced during your *originating event*. Some of us are very aware of what our *feared feeling* is because we are prone to feeling it much of the time. Others are less aware of it because our anxiety has ensured that we avoid situations that may prompt it. There are also those of us who simply deny its existence. Naming your *feared feeling* is useful in that, by doing so, you will be more in control of how you respond to the triggers and circumstances that prompt it.

The *feared feeling* that lies at the root of anxiety and panic can be one of many. However, there seem to be two core fears that are more common than others: *shame* and *grief*. Both have a huge influence on our self-esteem, the lack of which reduces are ability to protect both our physical and emotional boundaries, which invariably leaves us feeling less safe, more frightened and therefore more prone to anxiety and panic.

Shame

Shame is the emotion caused by the awareness of having had something dishonourable or humiliating done to us, or of having done something dishonourable or humiliating. For example, being bullied or bullying, being physically or sexually abused or abusing someone physically or sexually, being a victim of theft or of thieving, being deceived by someone or deceiving someone, being immorally treated or treating someone immorally.

Naturally, shame is influenced to a greater or lesser extent by cultural norms. The events that trigger it, however, are broadly speaking the same.

Guilt is similar to shame, the difference lying in that shame seems to be linked more to what others think and feel about what happened, whereas guilt seems more to do with how we feel about it ourselves. Naturally, the two are intertwined.

Grief

It could be said that all grief is triggered by some kind of loss. For example, the loss of someone in our life, the loss of something that afforded us security such as a home, an idea or a belief, the loss of confidence brought about by a significant or repeated defeat, the loss of respect or self-respect caused by shame, the loss of self-esteem due to a lack of love and attention, the loss of trust in others or in oneself due to deception, the loss of hope prompted by the seemingly impossible task of realizing a dream, or living up to other people's expectations, the loss of youth prompted by the onset of old age and the looming realization of our proximity to death.

Victim or victimizer

Anxiety and panic could, then, be described as the fear of being connected to painful emotions such as shame and grief, both of which influence our self-esteem and therefore our propensity to feel anxious and panicky.

The *feared feelings* that lie at the root of anxiety and panic are often prompted by events that have happened to us in the past and which were outside our sphere of influence. For example, a child being abandoned or an adult being assaulted by a physically stronger adult. Other times our *feared feelings* are prompted by things we have done ourselves. For example, abandoning a child or assaulting a person. In other words, we can consider ourselves as either a victim or as a victimizer. To a greater or lesser degree, most of us seem to have been both at sometime or other in our lives. Hence the vicious circle.

Whether you consider yourself more victim than victimizer, or the other way round, it will always be specific to specific events. That is to say that you cannot *be* a victim or a victimizer, you can only *experience* being one. The *Safe Space* procedure aims to empower you to take responsibility for how you feel about yourself in relation to the specific events of your choice.

Task 1: Naming your *feared feeling*

Some of you will already know what your *feared feeling* is. Sam, for example, identified shame as his *feared feeling* specific to the humiliating classroom experience. He identified grief as the resultant feeling from the loss of his stable, safe home due to his parent's acrimonious separation. Other examples of *feared feelings* are: feeling isolated, feeling trapped, feeling frightened that someone will harm you, feeling used, feeling powerless.

If you are able to identify and acknowledge your *feared feeling*, you will be less likely to repress it and more likely able to determine how you respond to those stimuli that trigger it.

If you are not yet able to identify your *feared feeling*, simply being aware that anxiety and panic can be mechanisms that enable you to avoid other more painful feelings can in itself prompt a shift in the way you understand your anxiety or panic.

Written Task

My feared feeling
My feared feeling is:

If you have been able to identify your *feared feeling*, you have already taken a big step towards overcoming your anxiety and panic. If you have not, the following steps will provide you with further opportunities.

The next *step*

This *step* has focused on that which lies at the root of your anxiety or panic. The next *step* focuses on the different aspects of yourself that you are going to employ to carry out the healing process. That is to say, your internal *family of selves.*

Step 4
My Internal Family of Selves

In this *step* you identify the needs, desires and resources of your *parent self, child self* and *protector*. The work done in this step prepares you for the tasks in *steps 5* and *6* in which you heal the past and take control of the present.

Part 1: My *parent self, child self & protector*

The task of naming and attributing characteristics to each member of your *family of selves* has two important functions. Firstly, by attributing specific needs, fears and desires to each *self* you are able to distinguish clearly between otherwise often confusing and conflicting emotions. Secondly, by creating an internal *family of selves*, you are effectively enabling these needs, fears and desires to communicate with one another. This is especially relevant in the next step, entitled *parenting the child,* in which your *parent self* and your *child self* exist simultaneously in the same story.

The act of fragmenting yourself into separate identities does not empower them with the ability to act autonomously without your consent. It merely enables you to call on particular aspects of yourself at particular times and for a particular purpose.

With regards to the *task* of characterising your *parent self*, you have already seen how the *parent self* has been given a *female* aspect and a *male* aspect. This is to highlight the fact that we are all composed of a collection of qualities and resources, regardless of gender. Naturally, most people have a dominant aspect. If you are a man, your dominant aspect is usually the *male parent self.* It you are a woman, it is usually the *female parent self.* This is not always the case though. Distinguishing between these two "*sub-selves*" is not an attempt to differentiate between men and woman, but simply uses those stereotypes often associated with men and woman to help identify different qualities.

Instructions

Fill in the following *task sheets.* Feel free to use your imagination. This task can be fun! The details marked optional are merely to enable you to better identify with the *self* and will not be required in order to carry out the subsequent tasks.

Task 1: Your *child self*

Written Task

My child self	Prompts & examples
Name	*e.g.* Sammy *as opposed to* Sam.
Character	*e.g. cheeky, polite, extroverted, introverted.*
Goals/dreams	*e.g. playing, being invisible, being a prince or princess.*
Values	*e.g. toys, friends, mummy and daddy, teddy.*
Needs	*e.g. to feel safe, to be looked after, to be loved, to be fed and clothed, to have parents.*
Desires	*e.g. to play, to explore, to learn, to experiment.*
Fears	*e.g. being alone, the dark, ghosts.*
Skills/resources	*e.g. imagination, spontaneity, energy, curiosity, having fun, living in the here and now.*
Responsibilities	*None*

Optional

Clothes	*e.g. pyjamas, trainers and t-shirt.*
Accessories	*e.g. a teddy bear, a toy.*
Voice	*e.g. speak more slowly or quickly; more seriously or more excitedly.*
Posture	*e.g. cross legged on floor.*
Mannerisms	*e.g. fidgeting.*
World view	*Begin with, "Life is..." or "People are..."*

Task 2: Your *parent self*

Written Task

	Male	**Female**	**Prompts & examples**
Name			*e.g Mr or Mrs. Sam.*
Character			*e.g. strong willed, intellectual, practical, nurturing, loving, co-operative, passive, active.*
Goals/dreams			*e.g. to have children, to be successful in at work, to be wealthy, to have a nice house.*
Values			*e.g. Honour, respect, love, friendship, trust.*
Needs and desires			*e.g. to be respected, to have a partner and friends, to have time alone., sex, to feel powerful.*
Fears			*e.g. not being respected.*
Skills/Resources			*e.g. will power, consistency, experience, logical thinking, physical strength. Ability to focus, multi-task, listen, soothe.*
Responsibilities			*e.g. to impose rules, to punish and reward, to nurture, to take decisions regarding the welfare of the child.*

Optional

Clothes			*e.g. Suit, uniform, casual clothes.*
Accessories			*e.g. a brooch or watch.*
Voice			*e.g. more serious or excited.*
Posture			*e.g. Upright or slouched.*
World view			*"Life is..." or "People are..."*

Task 3: Your *Protector*

Written Task

My *protector*	**Prompts & examples**
Name	*e.g. Cocky Sam.*
Needs	*e.g. to have something to protect, to be rewarded.*
Character	*e.g. aggressive, passive, loyal, irreverent, rebellious, timid.*
Skills/resources	*e.g. instincts, intuition, good memory.*
Responsibilities	*e.g. to identify and signal danger, to entertain, to aid in eliminating*

Optional

Main strategy type	*e.g. attacker; defender; peace offerer.*
Main strategies	*See list of popular protective strategies on pages 61 - 63. Choose as many options as you like. Add your own if you wish.*
Props and accessories	*e.g. a claw, a wand, a boxing glove, a bunch of flowers.*
Voice and language	*e.g. growling, seductive, barking, intelligent, articulate, matter-of-fact.*

The next step

The next step, entitled *parenting the child,* lies at the heart of the *Safe Space* procedure. It uses the component *selves* you identified in this chapter to "re-write" your *originating event* in a way that alters how you feel about your ability to cope in situations which appear to trigger the *feared feelings* you associate with the *originating event.*

Step 5
Healing the Past

The purpose of this *step* is to heal your relationship with the event that lies at the root of your anxiety in a way that the feelings you associated with the event no longer haunt the present.

This *step* includes an introduction and two *parts*. The introduction suggests some ways of healing the past. *Part 1* is a *visualization* and *part 2* a *written task*.

Introduction

Visualization or written task?

One of the most effective ways to change how we feel about the destructive behaviour of someone towards us or a particularly unpleasant set of circumstances is to confront the person in question or to change the circumstances. Unfortunately, this is not always possible. The people may no longer be alive and, if there are, a confrontation may be to traumatic or dangerous to consider. Likewise, the circumstances may have changed or be determined by too many uncontrollable forces for any kind of "real life" intervention to be worthwhile.

Both the *visualization* and the *written task* in this *step* aim to substitute a "real life" intervention. Of the two, the *visualization* is more likely to generate the intensity of feeling necessary for an emotional shift, without you running the risk of any "real" danger.

The *written task* has the advantage of permanence. It can also be useful in those cases where the *originating event* is particularly traumatic, or if you find visualizing particularly difficult. The *written task* can also serve as preparation for the *visualization*, or be used to re-enforce the work done in the *visualization.*

Parenting your child

Parenting your child consists of incorporating into your *originating event* your *parent self* in order to change the outcome of the event and thus your *child self's* experience of it. The term *child self* in this procedure refers to the *self* that experienced the *originating event,* regardless of your age at the time of the event.

There are many ways in which your *parent self* can intervene in order to heal the past. Sometimes this involves simply dialoguing with your *child self* or giving it a comforting gesture. Other times it may require speaking or acting on behalf of the *child self.* For example, it may involve creating or enforcing boundaries in order to stop *your child self* doing something, or in order to stop something being done to your *child self.* Alternatively, it may simply require providing your *child self* with unconditional love regardless of whether it fails or succeeds.

Whatever your *adult self* does or says, bear in mind that within the context of the *visualization*, your *adult self* and your *child self* act and feel autonomously.

Alternative interventions for healing the past

The following interventions include some of the most common ways in which your *parent self* can change the way your *child self* experiences an event. The term *culprit* refers to the person you feel caused you to feel your *feared feeling.* A *culprit*, in this context, may not necessarily have intentionally caused this feeling and their actions may have been effected by other people and events outside their sphere of influence at the time.

Change the outcome

The *parent self* changes the outcome of the event by stopping the occurrence of whatever caused distress to the *child self.* This effectively shows the *child self* that it can depend on the *parent self* to protect it should a similar threat arise.

Comfort the child self

The *parent self* changes the *child self's* experience of the event by reassuring the *child self* during and after the event that no matter what happens the *parent self* will still be there. Although this does not show the *child self* that it can rely on the *parent self* for protection, it does show the *child self* that it will not be abandoned.

Acquire justice

In cases when the *culprit* is a person or organization, the *parent self* can ensure that the *culprit* is punished in some way, or made to acknowledge privately or publicly what the *culprit* did. For example, having the culprit tried and sent to prison.

Release through forgiveness
The *parent self* forgives the *culprit* in order that release may take place. Sometimes, it is equally important to forgive the *child self* which, unwillingly, may have been at the root of subsequent future problems. For example, an abandoned child may, as an adult, find itself prone to abandon other people. Bear in mind that the purpose of forgiveness in this context is to let go of the pain and anger you may have been holding onto. In other words, it is yourself you freeing through forgiveness, not the *culprit.*

Understanding
The *Parent self* shows the *child self* an alternative interpretation of the events or offers an explanation for them. It may be that the *parent self* has other information at its disposal or because it has the capacity to look at the event from a different perspective and to see other reasons for why the event occurred. Shedding new light on the experience allows us to change our point of view regarding it. For example, someone's feelings about a person who attacked them may shift if they discovered that their attacker had themselves been the victim of a similar attack. Although this new understanding may not be sufficient to untangle the victim form their own strong feelings about the event, it may make it easier to forgive the *culprit.*

Example interventions

Bullying, assault, sexual abuse
You may wish your *parent self* to stand up to the *culprit*, and if this is physically not possible, to ensure that the *culprit* apologises publicly or privately, or is punished in some way and subsequently forgiven. The *parent self* could also say something that would show the *child self* that the problem lies with the *culprit.* Alternatively, the *parent self* could have the *culprit* explain their actions.

Accidents
In the case of having been the victim of an accident, or near accident, such as a car crash or a frightening plane experience, the mere fact that the *parent self* is present to reassure the *child self* may be sufficient to shift its experience of the event.

Self-inflicted abuse
Self inflicted abuse includes events which have been prompted by a lack of control or foresight. For example, a person who seems unable to say "no"

to other people crossing their boundaries, or a person who has difficulty determining where their own boundaries lie. In these cases, the *parent self* could clarify and maintain these boundaries.

Low self esteem caused by lack of love and affection
In those cases where there is a tendency for the *child self* to seek the love, affection and approval they lacked as a child by compulsively attempting to prove themselves worthy to others, the *parent self* could give the *child self* permission to fail and show the *child self* that it is valued and loved regardless of external outcomes.

Example of *Parenting the child visualization*

The following example of Sam's *Parenting the child visualization* contains some of the above interventions. Sam used as his *originating event* his humiliating classroom experience during which he wet himself when unable to recite the seven times table. The *visualization* was carried out with a hypnotherapist (myself). Rather than include the full transcript of the *visualization*, I have included a general overview. The completed version of Sam's own *written account* is included in *part 2* of this *step*.

> *Sam's Parenting the child visualization*
> Sam commenced his *visualization* when his classmate, Veronica, began reciting the eight times table. Sam positioned his *parent self* next to his seven year old *child self*. Sam's *child self* was not surprised to see an older version of himself standing next to him as trance logic, like dream logic, accepts as completely natural what would otherwise seem perplexing and illogical.
>
> When Sam's *child self* giggled at Veronica's stuttering, his *parent self* communicated to Sam that perhaps the reason for his giggling was that Sam was simply relieved it had not been him. The *parent self* communicated this in a kind, rather than disapproving manner and did not take the issue further.
>
> When Sam's *child self* was asked by the teacher to recite the seven times tables, the *parent self* did not take control of the situation or provide Sam with the answers. Rather, the *parent self* allowed the story to naturally unfold up to the point when Sam's *child self* wet himself. At this point the *parent self* communicated to the *child self* that he was aware of what had happened and that it was nothing to

be ashamed of. To emphasise this, the *parent self* held the *child self's* hand and did not let go until the end of the *visualization.*

When the *child self* was "ordered" by the teacher to wear the badge with the number seven on it until Sam was capable of reciting the times table, Sam's *parent self* intervened by confronting the teacher on the appropriateness of such a "punishment". The *parent self*, with the advantage of future hindsight, also communicated to the teacher what the future consequences of the "punishment" had been, and of how it was a particularly difficult time for Sam, i.e. that Sam's parents were in the process of separating. The teacher responded by saying that the badge was meant as an incentive rather than a punishment, and was sorry if it had been conceived otherwise. An agreement was reached that the *child Sam* would not have to wear the badge and that the *parent Sam* would help the *child Sam* revise his times tables.

Part 1: *Parenting my child* visualization

Accessing the past

In order to effectively visualize an event that took place in the past requires that we "regress" backwards in time to when the event took place. There are various ways in which we can do this while in a state of hypnotic-trance. One way is to count backwards by age or calendar years to the *originating event*, or to a happy experience just before the *originating event.* Alternatively, you can generate the feelings you associate with the *originating event* and use these feelings as a bridge through time to connect with the circumstances that originally triggered the feelings. This method, often referred to as the *Feeling bridge*, offers a quick and effective way to connect with the *originating event.*

The technique suggested for the *Parenting the child visualization* includes the use of an imagined timeline that stretches forwards into your future and backwards into your past. This technique is often referred to as *Timelining* and differs from the above techniques in that, as you regress backwards along the timeline, you are effectively "floating above" your past life and looking down at it. In other words, you exist as separate from and simultaneously to your younger *selves.* To control the regression backwards through time to the *originating event*, rather than counting backwards by age or calendar years, you go from one memorable event to another, looking down at your progressively younger *self* protagonizing each event. The procedure for this regression technique is included in the *task* instructions.

Healing the past

Once you have accessed the past, one way of healing your *originating event* is to have at your disposal all your present adult resources, knowledge, wisdom and understanding, and acting out the scene as the *child self* with an adult mind and resources. This technique is sometimes referred to as the *Adult resources technique.*

The technique suggested for *Parenting the child* is a variation of the *Adult resources technique.* It differs in that, rather than endowing your *child self* with your adult resources, the *parent self* drops down into the scene as an autonomous *self* and exists simultaneously with the *child self.* One of the advantages of this technique is that it enables you to clearly distinguish between the feelings of the *child self* that originally experienced the event and the role of the resourceful *parent self* whose responsibility it is to heal the past.

Task 1: Procedure for *Parenting your child* visualization

The following procedure is the same for those using self-hypnosis and for practitioners using hypnosis.

Visualization

Parenting my child visualization

1. Focus your mind on the originating event

Focus your mind on the circumstances surrounding the event you are going to use as your *originating event.* Decide upon where and when you are going to begin your *visualization.*

2. Explore ways of healing the past

Explore ways in which the *parent self* can intervene in order to heal the past. Identify what resources and skills it has at its disposal. The above *suggested interventions for healing the past* may prompt you with some ideas.

If you find it difficult to imagine how your *parent self* could intervene, think of those things you wish someone else would have done or said. These are the same things that your *parent self* can do.

***Parenting my child* visualization continued**

Bear in mind that, although you can pre-plan how your *parent self* is going to intervene, you may decide during the *visualization* to do something entirely different.

3. Connect with the resources of your *parent self*

You can do this in as subtle or exaggerated way as you like. For example, you could simply direct your intention towards those qualities you associate with your *parent self* by recalling occasions when you have successfully used them to achieve something or resolve a problem. In addition, you can wear those clothes you associate with your *parent self*. I once had a client who associated the qualities of her *parent self* with those of a queen, and who wore a tiara to connect with this "Queen self". This may seem slightly absurd to some, but when visualizing, just like in dreams, what may seem insignificant and meaningless when awake may seem profound and meaningful while in trance. Anything that helps you tap into your adult resources is worth considering.

4. Create your timeline

Your *timeline* floats above you and can be anything you wish it to be, so long as it has the quality of being able to stretch forwards into the future and backwards into the past. For example, a chord, a tunnel, a path, a beam of light, a railway track. To help identify with your timeline you may find it useful to visualize its colour and texture.

5. Focus momentarily on your *special place*

This *visualization* can sometimes prompt strong feelings to surface, which may threaten to overwhelm you.

This "release" may take place during the task or may take place hours, days of even weeks afterwards. In cases when strong feelings do emerge during the *visualization*, having your *special place* at the fore of your mind will enable you to more easily access it for some "time out". Remember, the aim of *Parenting the child* is *not* to re-experience painful emotions, but to experience the event that caused the emotions in a controlled, empowering way that allows you to release yourself from the hold they had over you.

Parenting my child **visualization**

6. Trance induction

Induce a medium level trance. Use the procedures for self-hypnosis or hypnosis set out in *Chapter 3*. For this *visualization*, the following sections are relevant: *Preparation - outside – eyes closed - inside – small things – different things – transforming things – in control of holding on – in control of letting go – prompt and explore special place – anchor special place – counting down from ten to zero (repeating in between the numbers the phrase "I am creating my timeline to take me back to my originating event".)*

7. Regress, as your *parent self*, back along your time line to the beginning of your *originating event*

When you reach zero, use your intention to create your *timeline* above you. Notice how it stretches forwards into the future and back behind you into your past. Use your intention to gather up the resources of your *parent self* and float up from your chair to your *timeline*. Notice your *physical self* sitting below. Use your intention to float back along your *timeline*, observing below the memorable scenes in your life playing themselves out, each scene containing a younger *self*. If the *originating event* is something that happened recently, substitute memorable events for ordinary everyday events. Regress back until just before your *originating event* is about to take place. From the safety of your timeline, take note of everything you see, paying special attention to your *child self*.

8. Have your *parent self* heal the past

Have your *parent self* drop down into the *originating event* below. BE THERE with your *child self*. Allow the scene to unfold and have your *parent self* intervene in whatever way you feel appropriate.

9. Unite the two selves and confirm that change has taken place

When the story has reached its conclusion, prompt your *child self* to literally "step inside" your *parent self* so as to become a single integrated individual. One way of doing this is to hug your *child self*. Notice how this feels.

It is essential here that the *child self* becomes part of the *parent self* of its

Parenting my child visualization

own accord. If it does not wish to, repeat the *task* using alternative interventions. Likewise, if you feel particularly uncomfortable having the *child self* as part of you, allow it step back out again and repeat the *task* using alternative interventions. You may wish to elicit from your *child self* what more it wants done.

If you feel comfortable with *your child self* inside you, rise up to your time line and look forwards along it to the present, noticing how your past may have been different because of the changes you have made. Then return along the timeline to the present until you are hovering once again over your *physical present self.*

10. Future progression

Look along your timeline into the future and notice what your see.

11. Return to present

Drop down into your *physical present self.*

12. Awakening

Counting up from one to ten – eyes open

Possible stumbling blocks for visualization

"I find it difficult to visualize my originating event"

If you are doing the *visualization* on your own, do not force yourself to visualize. You may simply not be in the right mood. Stop, and try again on another occasion.

"I feel overwhelmed and have to stop."

If possible, rather than terminate the *visualization*, access your *special place* by activating your *special place trigger* and spend as long there as you feel necessary in order to continue with the *task*. Never force yourself to do anything you do not want to. If after repeated attempts, you still find it difficult to visualize your *originating event*, you may want to entertain the idea of employing a professional practitioner.

Part 2: *Parenting my child written task*

The *written task* is for those of you who, for whatever reason, find it particularly difficult to carry out the *visualization.* It can also be used to reinforce the work done in the *visualization.* The procedure for the *written task* differs from that of the *visualization* in that it is carried out while in a fully conscious state.

Written Task

Parenting my child written task

1. Focus your attention on your _originating event_
Focus your mind on the circumstances surrounding the event you are going to use as your *originating event.* Decide where and when you are going to begin your *story.*

2. Explore ways of healing the past
Explore ways in which the *parent self* can intervene in order to heal the past. Identify the resources and skills it has at its disposal. The above *suggested interventions for healing the past* may prompt you with some ideas. If you find it difficult to imagine how your *parent self* could intervene, think of those things you wish someone else would have done or said. These are the same things that your *parent self* can do. Bear in mind that, although you can pre-plan how your *parent self* is going to intervene, your story may prompt you to do something entirely different.

3. Connect with the resources of your _parent self_
You can do this in as subtle or exaggerated manner as you like. For example, you can simply direct your intention towards those qualities you associate with your *parent self* by recalling occasions when you have successfully used them to achieve something or resolve a problem. In addition, you can wear those clothes you feel represent your *parent self,* just as you would wear the appropriate clothes when going to work or to a party.

4. Re-write your _originating event_ with your _parent self_ present
Write in present tense, as if were happening now. Use the first person (*I*) for your *parent self* and the third person (*he/she/name* of *child self*) when referring to your *child self.*

Parenting my child written task continued

Begin your *story* by describing the scene and those people present in as much detail as possible. Begin before your *child self* experiences the difficult feelings.

Remember that you are experiencing the story through the eyes of both your *parent self* and your *child self*. This *parent self* is not merely looking on, but present and pro-active in the story. Bear in mind that your *parent self* and your *child self* exist, act and feel independently from one another. Include in your *story* as much dialogue as possible between your *parent self* and *child self*, and between your *parent self* and other people in the story.

5. Uniting the two selves

When the scene has reached its conclusion, have your *child self* literally "step inside" your *parent self* so that you become a single integrated individual. One way of doing this is for them to hug one another. Describe how this feels. If you feel that more needs to be done in order to feel comfortable about merging together, add to or delete from your story whatever you think necessary.

6. Future progression

You may wish to extend your story into the future by creating a new chapter which begins in the present and continues into the future. Write this story in the first person as a single integrated individual.

Possible stumbling blocks for _Written task_

"I tend to get confused between my parent and child self"

In re-writing your *originating event*, the events are seen through the eyes of the *parent self*, not the *child self*. To avoid confusing the two, refrain from using pronouns such as *he* or *she* when referring to your *child self*. Instead, use its name. For example, Sam referred to his *child self* as Sammy.

Alternatively, you could use different colours for each of your two selves.

"I can't remember everything"

You do not need to remember all the details. What is important is the outcome of the story. Use your imagination to fill in the missing bits. Even names and descriptions of people you can invent if you wish.

"I keep reverting to the original story"
This is fairly common. So familiar are we with the *old story* that we often get carried along by it, as if it were a strong undercurrent. If this is the case, don't give up. The fact that you really have to work at changing the outcome suggests that change is taking place at a deep unconscious level.

"I keep putting off doing it"
At some level, most of us, if not all, attempt to avoid or postpone completing this *task*, often indefinitely. Again, this suggests that the act of carrying it out is meaningful and significant. Nobody can force you to do it, and nobody can do it for you. The responsibility lies with you and you alone.

Example: Sam's *Parenting the child* written task

Title: I do not feel ashamed
It is Thursday and Sammy, my seven year old *child self*, is in his maths class. Sammy has a stack of blond hair, is wearing flares and a blue and red school tie with a huge knot. Sitting next to Sammy is his friend Roderick, also in flares and double-knotted school tie. *I am standing next to Sam at the side of the table.* The maths teacher, Mr. Young, is standing at the front of the class by the blackboard. He calls out a student's name.

"Veronica," he says "the eight times table, please."

Veronica stands nervously. She isn't very pretty, wears glasses and stutters through the eight times table. Some boys at the back of the class begin giggling. Sammy tries to suppress his own giggles. He needs to go to the toilet. *I turn to face him.*

"Perhaps," I suggest, "the reason you are giggling is because you are relieved that it is not you that is standing up and reciting the eight times table. That's quite natural. And even if you do have to stand up, there is no need to worry. I am here with you."

Sammy continues to giggle. *I let it pass.* Sam is, after all, only eight. I catch sight of him holding his crutch and consider suggesting that he asks to go to the toilet. I reject the idea. Asking to go to the toilet for an eight year old can be embarrassing in its own way. Veronica stutters, successfully, to the end of the eight times table. Mr. Young, chalk in hand, surveys the class.

"Sam," he says. "The seven times table, please."

It takes Sammy a while to respond. He glances at me. *"Just try your best," I say. " If you do it, great. If not, it's not the end of the world."*

Sam slowly stands. He wants to hold onto his crutch but is too embarrassed to do so. The back-row boys begin their giggling.

"Don't worry about them," I say. "They are just relieved it's you and not them, and if it were them, they would be just as nervous as you."

Sammy begins his recitation.

"Ones times seven is seven," he says, without smirking. "Two times seven is fourteen. Three times seven is..."

Sammy's mind goes blank. His need to pee intensifies.

"Twenty-one," he finally says. "Four times seven is...." Sammy's face goes red. "Twenty-eight." He knows he is not going to make it. "Five times seven is...."

Sammy wets himself. *I take hold of his hand.*

"He can't continue," I say to the teacher.

Mr. Young concedes and Sammy sits down.

"David," continues Mr. Young. "Perhaps you would like to continue."

David stands up and breezes through the rest of the seven times table.

When the bell finally goes for the end of class, Sammy remains rooted to his seat. His friend Roderick tells him to get a move on if he wants to play football.

I intervene.

"He'll be along in a minute, Roderick. I just need to speak to him for a moment."

Roderick saunters out and loiters in the corridor outside. Left in the classroom are Sammy, Mr. Young and myself. Mr. Young is the first to speak.

"So Sam, what was it you found so funny?"

Sam glances at the door and thinks of running. *I intervene.*

"No need to run," I communicate silently. "Everything will be okay. Just tell him you didn't feel well."

"Nothing sir," says Sam to Mr. Young. "Sorry sir. I don't feel well, sir."

Mr. Young ignored the last comment and produced a badge with the number seven on it.

"What about this? Do you find this funny?" he said, holding out the badge for Sam to take.

Sam looked at the badge blankly.

"You will wear it," continued Mr. Young, "until you are capable of reciting the seven times table. Is that understood?"

I intervene.

"Perhaps we could continue this conversation at another time. Sam isn't feeling well and needs to go."

"This won't take a minute," replies Mr. Young, still holding the badge in his outstretched hand. *I intervene again.*

. *"Do you think this is appropriate? I say. "I mean, Sammy tried to recite the times table. Now he doesn't feel well and needs to leave. Maths may not be his best subject, but right now, making him wear that badge is not going to help him. I am afraid I insist. Sam needs to go with me."*

"The badge," the teacher replies, "is to motivate him, not to punish him."

"Yes, I can see how that may work for some students," I say. "But not for Sammy. And certainly not right now. I will help him with his maths personally, but I will not let you make him wear the badge. Now, please, let him go."

Mr. Young accepts my offer and allows Sammy to leave without the badge. Sammy thanks him, and runs passed Roderick to the toilets. Meanwhile, I find him another pair of trousers and meet him in the toilets.

"Here you are, Sammy?" I say, holding out a new pair of trousers for him.

Sammy smiles and step towards me. I embrace him and we become one. I do not feel ashamed. I feel okay.

Task 1: Your *New Script*

Instructions

Write your *Parenting the child new script* in the present tense. Use the first person (*I*) for your *parent self* and the third person (*he/she/name of child self*) when referring to your *child self.*

Written Task

My *Parenting the child* new script

Title:

The next step

In this *step* you have focused on healing the root of your anxiety or panic. The next *step* focuses on training your instincts in order that they respond appropriately to the triggers which previously connected you to your *originating event.*

Step 6
Training Instincts

This *step* focuses on your *Protector* and on positive feelings. It has three *parts*. In *part 1* you "train" your *protector* to respond to the commands of your *parent self*. In *part 2* you re-deploy the skills of the *protector*. *Part 3* offers a technique that enables you to access positive feelings and resources.

Part 1: Re-training my *Protector*

Training your *Protector* to respond to the commands of your *parent self* is like taming a dog or a horse because, essentially, the *Protector* is an instinctive and intuitive *self* that either "barks", "growls", "rears" or "bolts". These instincts, if not trained, will overpower the logic, reason and conscious will of the *parent self*.

In the following *task*, it is role of the *parent self* to "tame" the *protector* in a way that allows the *protector* sufficient autonomy to express itself (i.e. to sniff out and warn off impending danger), while at the same time respecting the wishes of the *parent self*.

The *task* is based on the belief that the *protector*, although a loyal friend who possesses highly evolved instincts and intuition, does not have the ability to self-reflect or to change how it behaves of its own accord. In cases of acute anxiety and panic, this *task* tends to be more effective if the cause of the anxiety and panic has already been treated in the previous *step*.

Preliminary exercise to foment belief

A good way of fomenting belief for this task is to carry out the exercise entitled *Foment belief* in the section *Safe Space procedure for self-hypnosis* of *Chapter 3*.

Task 1: Retraining your *protector*

Visualization

Retraining my *protector* visualization

1. Personify your protector

Choose either a dog or a horse to represent your *protector.* Visualize what this dog or horse looks like, and how it would respond to a potential threat such as another bigger animal. For example, would it bark, growl, bolt or rear?

2. Induce a light state of trance

Preparation - outside - eyes closed - inside – small things – different things – transforming things – in control of holding on – in control of letting go - counting down from ten to zero.

3. Task – Retraining my protector

3.1 *Protector personified as a dog*

If you chose a dog to represent your *protector*, choose either the scenario of a.) walking down a street full of people, or b.) driving a car down a busy road (your *parent self* is driving the car).

a.) Scenario of a street full of people with dog representing protector

Imagine your *parent self* is walking down a busy street. Of the many people you pass, most of them are wearing green coats, some are wearing red coats and one is wearing an orange coat. Those people wearing green coats and red coats are completely harmless. The one wearing an orange coats is probably harmless but may not be. The orange coat acts as a trigger to a past traumatic experience. Your *Protector* does not always distinguish between people in red coats and orange coats.

Have your *parent self* walk down the street with your *protector.* When the *protector* barks or growls at someone wearing a red coat, command him to stop or calm him by stroking him. When the *protector* does not growl at someone wearing a green or red coat, reward him with a pat, a stroke, some encouraging words or a small treat. When the *Protector barks* or growls at someone wearing an orange coat, thank the *Protector*, and simply avoid the person.

Retraining my *protector* visualization continued

b.) Scenario of driving a car down a busy road with dog representing protector.

The conditions and procedure here are the same as those in the above scenario only, instead of people wearing green, red and orange coats, the cars are of those colours.

Have the dog sit in the back seat. You may wish to include your *child self* in this *visualization.* If so, place it in the back next to the dog. Make sure that it is the *parent self* who gives commands to the dog and who hands out the punishments and treats.

3.2 *Protector personified as a horse*

Visualize your *parent self* riding the horse down a tree-lined avenue along which have been placed a number of orange traffic cones and one escaped orang-utan from a nearby zoo. The procedure is the same as the walking and driving procedure, except that the horse finds it difficult to distinguish between the orange cones and the orange orang-utans, the latter of which acts as the trigger to a past traumatic experience. If the horse rears or bolts at the sight of one of the cones, stop him doing so. If he does not, stroke him, pat him or give him a small treat. When the horse rears of bolts on seeing the orange orang-utan, control the horse but continue to avoid the orang-utan.

4. Awakener

Counting up from one to ten – eyes open

Possible stumbling blocks

"No matter how hard I try, I cannot control the protector"

This exercise often requires diligence and constant repetition. Don't give up.

Part 2: Re-deploying skills

Re-deploying skills is essentially the act of engaging the skills and resources of your *protector* in something other than alerting, eliminating, averting or avoiding perceived dangers. Re-employing skills works in much the same way as engaging a child in an activity to avert boredom or to deflect attention away from something else.

The *task* is based on the four following beliefs. 1.) The *protector* is a loyal friend that always acts according to what it believes is in the best interests of the individual. 2.) The *protector*, although the possessor of highly evolved instincts, does not posses the intelligence and the will to consciously analyse and change its own behaviour. 3.) For change to occur, it is easier to substitute old habits with new habits, rather than simply eliminate the old ones. 4.) Whatever changes affect the *protector* they must afford the *protector* a similar or better quality of life. That is to say, the *protector* can employ its skills and feel that it is an important, appreciated and respected member of the *family of selves.*

Task 1: Re-deploying the skills of your *protector*

Action

Re-deploying the skills of my *protector*

1. Focus on the skills and needs on your *Protector*

For example, the ability to detect danger and the need to feel that it is a respected member of the *family*.

2. Decide upon a new activity for your *protector* to employ its skills

Bear in mind that the primary skill of your *protector* is detection, thus the activity you choose should have this as its primary aim. If this condition is fulfilled, the activity can be anything you like. For example, spotting people with red hair, spotting car number plates with a particular combination of numbers or letters, looking out for police cars, listening out for particular words, identifying people wearing perfume.

Alternatively you can engage your *protector* in the act of designing something that detects and affords protection, for example, a castle or a home alarm system. This activity may seem a trifle strange, but as long

Re-deploying the skills of my *protector* continued

as the *protector* is actively engaged in an activity that employs its skills, it does not seem to mind what the activity is.

3. Thank the protector and introduce the new activity

Your *protector* is your loyalist friend that always acts with your best interests at heart. As such it is natural to thank the *protector* for its efforts, no matter how misdirected. By doing so, you are effectively conveying the message that the *protector* is an appreciated and important *family member* and it will therefore be more willing to accept its new task. One way of thanking the *protector* is to communicate the following.

"Thank you for doing such a good job of protecting us. I appreciate the time and effort you have put in. However, something has changed. I, the *parent* of the family, am here now to take on the responsibility of protecting the *child self*. Naturally, I will still need your skills and resources, but given that I am now here to help you, you no longer need to do everything on your own, and can now employ your skills in other more fun and creative activities. One of these activities is ....(activity).

Prompt your *protector* to engage in the activity when you feel you are at risk of feeling anxious.

Part 3: Feeling the way I want to

Accessing *desired feelings* can be done using the same principles upon which your *undesired feelings* are prompted except, rather than involuntarily connecting yourself to a traumatic experience, you voluntarily connect yourself to a pleasurable one.

Naming your *desired feeling* is an important part of the process of overcoming anxiety and panic as it provides you with something positive and tangible to focus on and cultivate.

Task 1: *Switching on* desired feelings

Switching on or connecting to your *desired feeling* is the act of flicking an internal "switch" that prompts you to change from how you don't want to feel to how you do want to feel.

Being able to *switch* from a debilitating feeling to an empowering one is possibly one of the most underrated and simplest ways of overcoming mild anxiety. It can also be used to thwart obsessive thoughts and compulsive behaviour. It is not effective for acute anxiety, panic or depression, certainly not as a long term solution. Nevertheless, having at your disposal a technique that you can use to determine how you feel is perhaps the closest we come to performing magic, albeit simply a trick of the mind.

The technique, common among neuro-linguistic programming (NLP) practitioners, is referred to in this book as the *switch technique.* It works in the same way that anxiety and panic are triggered by stimuli that connect us to a traumatic past event, except that we consciously and voluntarily anchor the trigger to a pleasurable event.

The act of triggering *desired feelings* is not something new. In fact, we naturally do it all the time. For example, a sportsperson who has just won an important point will often punch a raised fist into the air, and when they wish to call on the resources to enable them to win another point, they often clench the same fist.

In order to *switch* to your *desired feeling* you must first decide on what *switch* you are going to anchor it to. Examples of *switches* include; clenching a fist, squeezing or snapping two fingers together, squeezing an ear lobe, pressing a finger against your forehead, placing a hand on your heart. All may be accompanied by repeating to yourself a word or words you associate with your *desired feeling.* Bear in mind that your *desired feeling* is one that you may wish to access in public and thus it is advisable to make your *switch* as short, simple and natural as possible.

Written Task

My **desired feeling** is...
My **switch** is...

The *switch technique*

The following technique may appear to be no more than a trick of the mind and therefore unlikely to be substantial enough to deal with something as "real" and profound as anxiety. However, if repeated sufficiently, there are cases when it really does feel like magic.

Visualization or action

Switching on* my *desired feeling

1. Prime your *switch*

Priming your *switch* is the act of associating your *switch* with your *desired feeling*. This can be done by using hypnotic-trance to prompt your *desired feeling* or by utilizing "real life" experience.

Using hypnotic-trance to prime your switch

This method is the same as that for anchoring your *special place*. It differs in that instead of imagining your *special place* you create the conditions that you associate with your *desired feeling*.

Using experience to prime your switch

Anchoring your *switch* to a "real life" experience is the most effective way of priming your *switch*. Sam, for example, chose as his *desired feeling* that of being in the "in-zone", which he described as the experience of trusting his instincts while practicing sport. Whenever Sam was in this state, he primed his *switch*. Naturally, not all of us require such extreme conditions. One client, for example, who chose as her *desired feeling* that of "being at ease" required no more than a pillow, a good book and some light music.

2. Increase the effectiveness of your *switch*

The effectiveness of the *switch technique* is dependent upon repetition. The more times you prime it, the more effective it is. Like a watch, if you don't wind it up, it will stop working.

3. Flicking your switch

When you wish to *switch* to your *desired feeling*, it is often because you are experiencing another feeling you do not wish to experience, such as anxiety or panic. It makes sense, then, to *switch off* this *undesired feeling* at

Switching on my _desired feeling_ continued

the same time as *switching on* your *desired one.* To achieve, use your intention to transfer your *undesired feeling* into a hand and, as you breath out, symbolically flick the feeling away. Then, as you breath in, connect to your *desired feeling* by "flicking" your *switch.* Repeat the process as many times as necessary to achieve a transition from one feeling to another.

Next step

In *steps 5* and *6* you have worked to change your relationship with your past, you have retrained your instincts to respond appropriately, and learnt ways of accessing positive feelings. The next *step* confirms and reinforces theses changes.

Step 7
The Future

The purpose of this step is to reinforce and confirm the changes you have made thus far. It contains three *parts.*

Part 1 offers two *visualization* techniques. The first enables you to progress forwards in time and glimpse how your *new self* might experience life. The second substitutes your *old story* for your *new story. Part 2* introduces affirmations as a means or reinforcing your *new beliefs. Part 3* uses "real life" experience to confirm that change has taken place.

Part 1: My *new self* and my *new story*

Your *new self* is the *self* that exists as a consequence of the changes you have made. Although this *self* does not have a history or set of memories that serve to reinforce its existence, it is possible to glimpse how your future may be different because of the existence of this *new self.*

The notion that we can glimpse the future may seem like an odd one and, for some, an impossible or even dangerous one. The notion is based on the idea that the future can take one of many paths, each of which is determined to a greater or lesser extent by the decisions we act upon as individuals, whether consciously or unconsciously. Naturally, there are many unpredictable and uncontrollable forces that will effect our progress into the future, but how we respond to them is determined by how we feel about them, how we feel about ourselves and by what skills we have at our disposal to deal with them.

Glimpsing the future, then, refers to how we would respond to it, and not to how it will be.

Task 1: Seeing though the eyes of your *new self*

The following *visualization*, sometimes referred to as *Open door*, uses the power of the imagination to look into the future through the eyes of your *new self.*

Visualization

Seeing through the eyes of my *new self*

1. Induce a light level trance

Preparation - outside – eyes closed - inside – transforming things – small things – different things – in control of holding on – in control of letting go – counting down from ten to zero.

2. Task

Approach the home of your future self.

As you *count down from ten to zero, imagine yourself approaching the home of your future self.* This home may be the same one you live in now, or maybe a different one. Whether it is old or new, notice any changes or differences, for example, the design or colour of the door.

Meet your future self.

Knock on the door or ring the bell. The person who opens the door is your *future self* who exists as a consequence of the personal development work you have done. Whether this *self* exists somewhere in the near or distant future, he/she is happy to see you. Notice how your *future self* looks, paying special attention to how he/she is standing and what he/she is wearing or holding

Become your future self.

Your *future self* invites you in, gesturing you to follow him/her. As you follow behind, you gradually get closer and closer until you physically step into the back of your *future self* and become your *future self.* Take time to look around through the eyes of this *future self.* Explore each room, look in the fridge, the wardrobes, under the bed, on the shelves, in the garden. Notice any differences. If there are other people in the house, notice how they respond to you.

3. Awakener

Find somewhere in your home to lie down and have your *future self* close his/her eyes Count up from one to ten and open the eyes of your present physical *self.*

Task 2: Substituting your *old story* for your *new story*

The object of this *task* is to re-run your *old story* with your *new self* as protagonist. Before carrying out the *task*, be sure to have revised the details of your *old story*. This task is much like the *Miracle script in Step 1* only, rather than a miracle having occurred, the change is a consequence of the personal development work you have done. The *task* can also be carried out as a continuation of *Task 1*.

Visualization

Substituting my *old story* for my *new story*

1. Induce a light level trance

Preparation -outside – eyes closed - inside – transforming things – small things – different things – in control of holding on – in control of letting go – counting down from ten to zero.

2. Task

Follow the same procedure as in *task 1* for approaching the home of your *future self*, meeting your *future self* and becoming your *future self*.

Re-run the events of your *old story* as your *new self*.
When you carry out this part of the *task*, make sure that your *parent self* is the predominant *self* and use whatever commands or calming strategies you require to control your internal *protector* and to reassure your internal *child self*. Carry out the *task* as a single integrated individual.

3. Awakener

Find somewhere to sit or lie down, have your *future self* close his/her eyes, count up from one to ten and open your eyes as your present physical *self*.

Part 2: My new beliefs

Change can be gradual and take a bit of getting used to. Indeed, some people who have overcome anxiety and panic find it odd and, at times, even surreal to find themselves feeling okay. Other times anxiety and panic seem to disappear almost instantaneously and magically, never to return with the same intensity. On occasion, especially in those cases when the root of the problem has not been sufficiently treated, anxiety can return gradually or suddenly.

Whatever the future holds in relation to your anxiety and panic, it is advisable to use as many techniques as possible to ensure that change is permanent. One such strategy is to affirm your *new story* by repeating any new beliefs you hold concerning it. This repetition of a belief is referred to here as an *affirmation* and usually consists of a single word or a short sentence. For example, *It is my intention to take responsibility for how I feel.*

By repeating an *affirmation* periodically and consistently, it effectively "brainwashes" the unconscious mind to function in accordance with the message it conveys. Like a child, if the unconscious mind is told something enough times it will come to perceive it is true. Naturally, this technique can be used negatively and destructively, especially if the affirmations are hidden or embedded in some other message. Here, however, the affirmation is uttered consciously and with intention.

Affirmations can take many forms. A prayer or mantra can be an *affirmation. Affirmations* can be sung. Even orders and instructions can be *affirmations* if they are repeated enough times. *Affirmations* can be silent and they can be uttered out loud. You can also carry out your *affirmation* in conjunction with a symbolic act. For example, if the *affirmation* contains the intention to let go of an *undesired feeling*, you may wish to symbolically destroy the feeling by writing in down on a piece of paper and burning it. One client of mine who felt that someone else had "dumped" their feelings onto him/her, went so far as engraving the feeling onto a stone and burying it in the garden of the "rightful owner".

For an *affirmation* to be effective, it helps that it is short, simple and concise, preferably no more than one sentence. Try not to include the words *if, but, although* or *were it not for.* A good way to start an *affirmation* is with the words, *I am* or *It is my intention to.*

Although the content of the *affirmation* is important, the effectiveness of an *affirmation* depends primarily on repeating it consistently and periodically.

Example affirmations

Sam's affirmation for helping him to accept his new relationship to his *originating event* was the following:

I am responsible only for that which I can control.

The following list of *affirmations* may prompt you to come up with your own.

I do not take responsibility for other people's actions that are outside my control.
I take responsibility for how I feel about my past.
My protector is not my master.
It is my right to move on.
I will no longer be held back because of something someone else did.
I will no longer carry around with me feelings of guilt that do not belong to me.
I will not return to pick up that which I have left behind.
I am in the driving seat of my car, not in the seat of anyone else's.

Task 1: Affirming your new beliefs

Instructions

To affirm your new beliefs and intentions, create an affirmation that conveys them in a simple, concise manner. Decide how many times a day you are going to repeat the *affirmation*, at what times of day and for how many days. For example, three times a day at nine o'clock in the morning, at mid-day and nine o'clock in the evening, for a period of one week.

Written Task or Visualization

Affirming my new beliefs

My affirmation is:

Number of times:

Times of day:

Number of days:

Part 3: Confirming that change has taken place

Confirming that you have begun a *new story* in which you no longer experience anxiety or panic in a debilitating way is as equally important as creating the change itself. Confirmation usually takes place naturally when you discover that the triggers that you identified in your *old story* no longer seem to prompt anxiety or panic. Often this discovery is accompanied by a slightly odd feeling that takes some time getting used to, rather like wearing a new pair of shoes which you really like but which require some time to wear in.

If confirmation of your change is not immediate and natural, it is sometimes necessary to prompt it by deliberately re-running the circumstances of your *old story* in order to experience your *new story*. The earlier you substitute your *old story* with your *new story* the quicker you will reverse the downward spiral of panic and anxiety, and with time new habits will engrave themselves into your psyche, just as old habits did.

If you are able to confirm that change has taken place but find that you are still experiencing some mild anxiety, don't worry. Your *new story* has already begun to substitute your *old story*. All you need to do is allow time run its course until the *old story* exists merely as a distant memory.

If you find that your anxiety and panic are only slightly less intense, and barely manageable, this does not necessarily mean that your efforts have been in vain. Sometimes the process of substituting your *old story* with your *new story* takes some time.

It may also be that this process has not had the effect you had wished for. Very few methods, if any, suit all people. Do not give up. Whatever the outcome of your efforts, something will have shifted, and this will gradually seep into your life and enrich your experience of it.

Epilogue

It is my personal opinion that those individuals who are brave enough to acknowledge and confront their own fears are the true heroes and heroines of our time.

Traditionally, heroes and heroines have been applauded for their courage and conviction in the face of danger and adversity. They are intrepid explorers who have crossed the deepest oceans or climbed the highest mountains in search of new horizons. They are warriors and soldiers who have fought against all odds for what they believe in. They are princes who have slain dragons and martyrs who have died for a cause. They are thinkers and believers who advance alternative visions of how life could be. Such heroes and heroines, whether real or fictitious, are no doubt worthy of their heroic status, of the stories told of them, the monuments sculpted, poems recited and songs sung. What unites these heroes and heroines is that they all strive towards an alternative future, and to achieve it they must risk something, whether it be their own life, their pride or their wealth.

The same is true for those individuals who acknowledge and confront their fears. They may not have to sacrifice their lives, but they often have to let go of a way of living their lives. They too get to expand horizons and forge new paths towards an alternative future. They too are fuelled by the conviction that things do not have to be how they have always been, and that change is possible. Their stories may not be recorded in the annuls of history, but they do get to write their own. They get to grow and evolve into more balanced, aware, accessible, less defensive and often kinder human beings. No matter how little or great their growth is, they grow, and whatever their story, it is difficult not to feel admiration for them.

Some people believe they are too old to change. Indeed, it may be true that the older we get, the more fixed we become in our ways, the more liable we are to hold firm to old beliefs, the more skilled we become at navigating around our fears. We also become more vulnerable to illness and loss, more aware of the inevitable passage of time and how unresolved issues seem to expand and spread, inevitably surfacing as some symptom or other, until death. Yet, however old we are, our ability to grow never seems to wane. On the contrary, the additional wisdom and experience makes change not only easier, but often more rewarding and heroic.

I hope the model and procedure offered in this book has helped you to create the change you desire, however great or small it is. If, indeed, you have gone some way to overcoming your anxiety and panic, you have therefore taken greater responsibility for how you feel on your path through life, and this will affect the people you meet along the way.

As travellers on life's highway, what sets you apart is not how far along you are, but the distance travelled.

Contents

Detailed version